MW00618431

Momma's Love

Written by

Queen Carm

Based on a True Story

Momma's Love

For more information, contact: 1queencarm@gmail.com

ISBN-13: 978-1-7367961-0-8

Printed in the USA

DEDICATION

This book is dedicated to the younger me. Everything I went through as a child, the things that I heard, and saw were all for a purpose. I have conquered my past and overcome all the pain. I appreciate the healing process I experienced throughout the years. I am proud of my growth and the woman, and mother I have become. I began writing this story throughout my depression and grief recovery of losing My Granny. I wrote this book to cleanse my soul and my mental from the traumas of my past. I wrote this book for the mothers before me whose stories went untold.

This book is dedicated to my daughters and my nieces. I love you! Please know and understand, no mother is perfect. God gave us our mother for a reason. It is up to you to decide which examples are good and bad. You will get to create your own path to become the woman you want to be proud of.

To every one of the young women stuck in generations of cycles that you are not even aware of. You can overcome the broken cycles set before you and thrive beyond your own fears and imagination. For the women that recognizes their family's broken cycles and is willing to end it with their mother to make a difference for the generations of your children's children.

I learned some very valuable lessons while creating this

story. Your journey is your story, and it cannot be changed. Do not carry any shame. Sometimes courage will skip a generation. Only you can tell your story. Not as a victim but as an achiever and conqueror. There is power in releasing your pain.

Thank you to my readers, for believing in me to purchase my first book.

I pray my story inspires you, uplifts you, and helps you in some way. Blessings to you.

The most powerful person in the world is the storyteller. The storyteller sets the vision, values, and agenda of an entire generation that is to come.

~ Steve Jobs

PREFACE

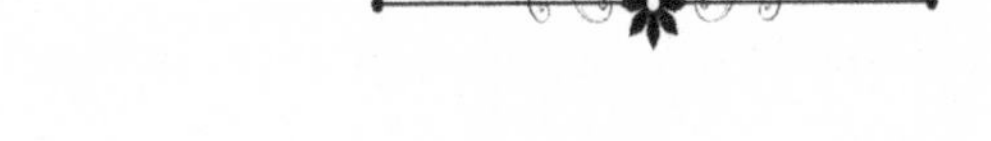

Love: *a profoundly tender, passionate affection for another person. A feeling of warm personal attachment or deep affection, as for a parent, child, or friend.*

Nurture: *to feed and protect; to support and encourage, as during a period of training or development; foster; to bring up; train; educate.*

Motherhood is the most important job that God blesses a woman with. It is an opportunity to share her unconditional love and raise a child. From the first kick in her womb to the baby's date of birth, every emotion is shifted onto that innocent baby. Raising a child is a full-time role and comes with many amazing—and some not so exciting—moments. The entire journey is a blessing in its special way. Every thought, every word taught, and every action displayed will affect the child as it develops over the years. Nurturing and giving love to a child is important, as it will leave an imprint and everlasting impact. As a mother, your role begins after your positive pregnancy test and does not end until death.

Your legacy will be your children, and who they become as adults. Every lesson that a child learns, good or bad, will impact how they see the world, how they interact with people, and most importantly, how they view you, their mother. Right or wrong. There is no perfect answer or instructional guide to being a mother. You do the best you can and later, your children will be the determining factors of how good a job you did raising them. How they feel about you will eventually come out. How your daughter sees you will determine her future, her potential mothering skills, and how she views you for the rest of her life. Every daughter is entitled to have an opinion of her mother.

Mothers are the only people in your life that cannot be replaced.

TABLE OF CONTENTS

INTRODUCTION

We are all in the same story, with a different point of view.

Generational division—the generations before not telling their story, including bits and pieces as situations arise, leaves new generations not having a clue about their history. No answer to the whys and hows. Carrying demons of the past with no guidance on how to battle them.

All families deal with them. No one wants to discuss them. They're the weighted chains. Generations of repeated cycles. The battles of the generations before you. Some even call them curses. It is dealing with a demon that did not come from your experience, but your history. Now you are a product of somebody else's decisions, having insecurities based on someone else's historical experience. What is not transformed is transferred. You must transform the picture of the family.

A child is not responsible for their existence; their parents are. Many of us will engage in conversations about deadbeat dads quickly and with proven facts. I want to make it fair and address both parents, but most importantly, the mothers. No, not deadbeat moms; that is not my lane. I'm talking about the nonexistent relationship with emotions, nurturing, and affection that daughters can receive from their mothers. It continues to pass along to the next generations.

The struggles of single motherhood are real. Growing and creating yourself as you raise children. Raising children while carrying generations of heavy burdens and cycles of damage. The failings of a mother, from one generation to another, cause a lack of understanding of who a person is as an individual and as a woman. The load of brokenness being passed down from one generation to the next without anyone intentionally trying to hurt the next, but ignorant to the future reality.

Single moms must be cautious about what they are showing their children. Moms are never fully aware of exactly what their children see, and the innocence of a child should always be protected. The examples set will affect them and their future; the habits taught them follow throughout their teenage years and adulthood.

Women are carriers of everything. Love, babies, burdens, baggage, emotions, thoughts—everything! Every generation is being raised to have it all together, missing the point that it's okay not to have it all figured out. Carrying a load of toxicity without knowledge of such actions, projecting imperfections and flaws, all while creating damaged goods. Yes, the cycles continue from one generation to the next, subconsciously. You've got to heal from the hells of the generations before you in order to create and follow the new paths for yourself and generations to come.

From the moment you find out you are pregnant, everything is a choice. The decision to become a mother creates a lifelong career into motherhood. To decide to have a baby is a lifelong decision. Your job as a mom never ends. And you are never truly prepared for the role of becoming a mom.

CHAPTER 1

This story begins with Louise. Born to a hardworking single mother, Louise had early memories of her mother catching a bus to the cotton fields to work where she labored, sweating all day in the hot, Alabama sun with blistering, rough fingers. She was raised in a family where you were taught to not tell anyone what you were going through. Mothers did not talk to and teach their daughters the ways of life. It was simply go to church, find a job, and start a family.

Louise grew up the youngest of twelve. Her entire family all lived on one block. Grandparents, aunts, uncles, and cousins were right next door or down the street. Being raised by a single mother with the help of family, many cycles began. She did not have a father around as a little girl, and grew up not knowing she was trying to fill a void.

A rebellious soul, Louise was a tough, sweet, sarcastic, independent woman. Dating was her way of having a personal life. She got married when she fell in love and accepted a few of their rings and last names. Louise did not stay married long because she enjoyed her freedom more, living by her own rules and constantly creating new ones. By the time she was thirty, she had six children: four boys and two girls, with five different fathers. Louise was done having children.

Like most single Black mothers, she worked hard, provided for her children, and went to church, never dealing with her own childhood experiences; not being able to fully heal from how she was raised by her mother and absent father. Louise buried her silent tears and childhood pain as she got older. She was taught to maintain a smile on her face through internal pain and mental wars. Hide your flaws and show no imperfections. She had skeletons in her closet too. Anything that she was ashamed of was not mentioned or passed down to teach her daughters not to do. It happened, she learned from it, and pushed it out of her mind as if it didn't happen and everything was okay. She became a woman and a mother but did not heal from her childhood or the cycles set before her.

Louise was focused on her career, her appearance, and at times, a man. Not to confuse her lack of nurturing with being a provider, she provided her children with the necessities of life throughout their childhood.

Louise was a good mother in the eyes of her children. She told them I love you often. Always hugging and kissing them to show them affection that she wished she received from her mother. She was always in the stores shopping for them—many times, buying them things they did not need. Louise overcompensated for their absent fathers more than she realized. Her children had everything they needed and some of their wants, although they were upset with her that their fathers were not around like other children.

Louise was the type of mother to go without before her children went without something. Her children did not wear hand-me-downs unless it was from their older sibling. She encouraged them to be whatever they desired in life, always trying to make them feel good and confident about themselves.

Learned behaviors are passed down and accepted by the next generation. All her children were smart in school, helpful at home, and well-behaved in public. Raising her children in the Church and teaching them about God was important to Louise. That's how she was raised.

Louise did not teach her kids worldly information. There were a lot of things that she could have taught her children about the world. Having to figure everything out on her own, she did the same to her children. Being taught not to share information, she didn't inform or explain much to them.

Momma Louise became an entrepreneur early in life as a beautician. Growing women's natural hair and making them feel good about themselves was her specialty. When her children were young, she worked at home, having a small beauty salon built in her home.

Responsibilities came early in life. Louise raised and disciplined them to clean the house, cook, change a diaper, and be a good student. By the time the oldest was 10, she would leave them home alone. The older children handled the responsibility of taking care of their younger siblings. With family close by, the children were fine home alone.

Louise's Place of Beauty was a small store front salon located in a shopping plaza just seven minutes from her home. The salon held four stylist booths, two hair dryers, and two shampoo bowls. The entrance of the salon had enough room for a small sitting area and snack vending machine.

Owning her beauty salon in town, she worked day and night to provide for her children. Every day at the salon, she listened to gossip about the lives people were living from her clients and the other stylists. She would listen about people's children living promiscuously, hooked on drugs, or living on the street. Plenty of poor choices that she did not want her children being exposed to. Some nights she came home late, after the children had eaten dinner, cleaned the house, and were already in bed.

Louise raised her children, and they became adults: parents, wives, and husbands. They each had their idea of what type of adult they wanted to be and the goals they wanted to accomplish. Momma Louise's personal decisions affected both of her two daughters. As soon as they turned 18, they both caught the first bus away from their hometown, getting married in their early 20s and starting families of their own.

There is no perfect answer to motherhood. You do the best you can and later on, your children will be the determining factor of how they feel about you as their mother.

Louise survived through her own set of challenges in life while becoming a better woman and raising children, shuffling cycles down to the next generation of children without recognizing the childhood traumas and experiences she was creating. And so, they continued . . .

CHAPTER 2

Mabel was the third-oldest of Louise's six children. Growing up, she witnessed and formed an opinion of her mother's lifestyle. Mabel paid attention to her mother's career choice, how she took care of herself, and most importantly, how her mother treated her. Everything was under surveillance by her daughter. Mabel knew exactly what she wanted to do differently for herself. Her number one goal was to get married and have children with just one man. She did not care for many of her mother's choices and examples. She strove to be different from her mother, but was similar in countless ways by genetics.

Mabel followed in her mother's footsteps and became a cosmetologist, focusing on herself through trade school but learning and exploring. She met her first and only boyfriend, Raymond Maxwell.

Raymond Maxwell was the youngest of five children and the only boy in his family. His parents married early in their 20s and stayed married for 75 years until death did they part. Momma Ella was a sweet, soft-spoken woman. She stayed home all day taking care of her children, keeping a clean home, and cooking. Life was simple for Ella Maxwell. Papa worked every day, all day. He maintained his farmland and sold what the farm produced: milk, eggs, vegetables, and fruits. He was a handyman and could fix anything around the house. He provided for his family as he was raised to do.

Papa was a drinker, and always kept a bottle of whiskey hidden in the house.

Raymond was taught to go to school and how to care for the crops and animals. He was taught how to be a man and a provider by his father. He was a tall and strong teenager. Papa showed him how to do everything with his hands. Raymond took pride in being a handyman. He could fix anything he touched, so after high school, he went into a career in construction.

Every Sunday they went to church as a family. Raymond and Mabel met at a church event. Despite her initial resistance, Raymond remained a gentleman and was persistent in going after the woman he yearned for. They had a lot of similar qualities, including a strong relationship with God. They quickly fell in love and got married. Just a few months after their vows, Mabel gave birth to their first child, Whitney. Together, they were a family and supported one another, providing a foundation for their children and an example for future generations.

Becoming a mother at 21, Mabel was forced to look at life differently. She was now responsible to teach someone else about life. All she had was her mother's examples and words. She adapted to some of her mother's ways as she began to experience motherhood, making a few changes of her own while evaluating every step during motherhood.

Mabel quickly had to decide between her family or a career and like most women, she wanted both. After having two more children, Samantha and Ray Jr., Mabel and Raymond agreed that three children were enough. They both came from large families, so they were aware of the struggles and hardships of raising a lot of children.

Ready to get back to her independence and career, Mabel returned to the salon when Ray Jr. was a toddler. Every week she worked Tuesday through Saturday. In addition to accomplishing parent-teacher conferences, press and curls, and running to the church throughout the week, Mabel was active in her children's lives and education. She was a busy woman and stayed on the go, like her mother.

Mabel was focused on loving her children and giving them a life that she did not have. She was not unsatisfied with how her mother raised her, she just wanted more, and her version of better. Just as Momma Louise did, she tried to protect her children from the cold, cruel world. Mabel and Raymond strove to keep their children focused on their education, religion, and making something of themselves.

She was pleased with the life she was living. Whitney, Samantha, and Ray Jr. were the products of a two-parent home. Together, Mabel and Raymond earned good salaries, lived in a Black suburban neighborhood, and sent their children to private schools. Mabel traveled with her family, wanting to expose her children to a life she'd desired when she was a little girl. Life for the Maxwell family was their version of perfect.

CHAPTER 3

Whitney was the oldest daughter born to Mabel and Raymond Maxwell. As she grew up, she too formed an opinion of her mother's lifestyle and behaviors. Together, they carried firm values in education, Church, and family. Whitney was unhappy with how she was raised, upset that she was the oldest and had to help with her younger siblings at times. She disliked that she attended private schools and wore uniforms from elementary to middle school. Whitney believed in and loved God, but she did not want to go to church multiple times during the week. She didn't want to follow in her mother's footsteps to do hair either. Everything that Mabel displayed to her daughter, Whitney vowed to do the complete opposite, creating her own rules to live by.

After graduating high school, she went off to college. Papa Ray bought her a car after graduation. Not knowing what she wanted to do or how to go about doing anything, she started her journey. Wanting to stay close to home, she went to a local community college a few hours away from her hometown. She drove home on weekends to hang out with her friends from high school. Whitney enjoyed attending parties and drinking. She met Charlie Randolph at a friend's house party. Within a few short months of dating, they were in love.

During her sophomore year of college, she completed

advanced classes and earned an associate degree. Unsure about staying at school or starting her career, Whitney moved back home. She began working as an accounting clerk for a law firm downtown. She was good with math and numbers.

Whitney and Charlie were raised differently, but both were raised in a two-parent household. Their once loving relationship soon turned toxic after Whitney found out she was pregnant. Most likely I was conceived on or around my father's birthday, because my birthday is exactly nine months after his. During Whitney's sixth month of pregnancy, Charlie began to physically abuse her. He started taking his frustrations out on her, hitting her whenever he was upset. Charlie would apologize and no matter what, he would hit her again. I was being birthed into confusion and conflict.

Most women would rub their belly, sing, and sometimes read so their unborn baby can hear her voice, wanting their unborn baby to feel love and compassion as it continues to grow inside of her. Not my mother. The first feeling of being unwanted and alone in the womb was only the beginning. A mother's love for her child should be unconditional. Subconsciously, love can come with conditions by design.

On my birthday, I was born to Whitney Maxwell and Charlie Randolph. They named me Khloe Randolph. I was the perfect blend of both of my parents. I got my daddy's complexion, deep dimples, and long toes. I was born to two young adults who knew nothing about loving, nurturing, or raising me. I was born into the world knowing absolutely nothing. It was up to my parents to teach me everything. My journey began.

My parents and I lived with Grandma Lily, Daddy's mother. Lily had divorced Grandpa Charlie long before I was born. Charlie Sr. was an "abusive, self-centered asshole," she once said. Being with my parents was always loud, angry, hard-headed, and aggressive. I hated it! Momma was always irritated with me no matter what I did. Daddy was always yelling at her. I did not understand why they were always yelling. I watched Momma cry a lot. Almost every day there was an argument about something. If my clothes were dirty, Daddy was yelling at Momma to wash me up and change me. When Daddy would come home, Momma would fuss at him to get me so she could get a break. It was every day, nonstop fighting with my parents. When Grandma Lily was home, she would tell them both to shut the hell up!

Physically fighting was how they ended their arguments. Daddy would sit me in the bathroom and close the door during their fights. Sad and alone, I would sit in the empty, cold tub, cover my ears, and just cry. I didn't want them to fight. Sitting in the tub felt like forever. When it got quiet, I would open the door. The room would be a mess and Daddy was gone. I would pick up toys and play while Momma just cried and even screamed in anger.

There were times when I was in the room during the arguing and fighting. They did not care enough to not fight in front of me. I would cry and scream for them to stop, tears flowing from my eyes. Screaming did not make the fighting stop. I had no choice but to sit there and watch Daddy hit and choke Momma. She rarely tried to fight back but when she did, it only made the beatings worse.

The first time I told Grandma Lily that they were fighting and what I saw, she told me to go sit by her bedroom door so I did not have to see what was going on. She usually kept her door locked so Charlie would not go in her room when she was not home. She asked him enough times not to snoop through her room until she finally put a lock on her door.

The next day when the yelling and pushing started, I grabbed a blanket from the couch and sat on the stairs by Grandma's bedroom, even falling asleep. Witnessing these fights between my parents was scary as a toddler. They did not like one another, and it was obvious.

A few weeks later, I was sitting on the stairs by Grandma Lily's bedroom door, wishing she were home or that her bedroom door was unlocked. It was early, and I could hear Momma and Daddy yelling back and forth at one another already. Daddy was yelling loudly about dirty clothes. "You told me you were going to do the laundry. Why the fuck can't I find my shirts if you washed them?" he yelled.

Momma just kept saying, "I washed your clothes last week. I'm not wearing them for you too!" SLAP! There was a loud thud on the floor, and she cried louder, followed by a few more hard bumps into the walls. The door was slammed so hard, it shook the windows on the house.

I was numb to the sounds of the fighting. I could see their shadows on the walls of the stairwell, but I did not want to peek my head around the corner. Momma screamed, "FUCK YOU TOO!" and cried loudly.

I scooted down the stairs slowly and quietly. I saw her

sitting on the bottom step with her head in her hands, sobbing uncontrollably. She was praying and calling on Jesus. When I rubbed the back of her hand, she jumped up and moved away from me. It was like she forgot that I was in the house. She looked at me as if I had done something wrong. I wanted to console my mother. I wanted her to stop crying. Instead, she treated me like a nuisance. Momma wanted nothing to do with me and her body language said it all. I was two years old.

During the first few years of my life, I spent time with my parents separately. Never together as a family.

I always enjoyed being with my Grandma Lily. She was the best granny and my favorite person in the world. Grandma Lily always expressed love that would warm my heart and put a smile on my face. She kept a cup of coffee close and a cigarette burning throughout the day. We would sit on her bed and watch cop shows and game shows together. It was peaceful with Grandma, and I was always happy to be with her. Wherever she went, I was right there with her. Grandma Lily would go to the supermarket every Saturday morning for groceries and her Sunday dinner. If I were awake and dressed, I would go with her. Grandma cooked dinner every day and made sure I had snacks.

Daddy was a quiet man when he wasn't yelling at Momma and he looked mean all the time. He had bad teeth and a big, bald head. We only spent time together when Momma was at work. He never played baby dolls with me, but we colored together. Grandma bought me crayons and coloring books. Daddy showed me how to color in the lines. He said the picture looked perfect when you colored it in one direction. I enjoyed coloring and expressing myself through the art of the different colors and picture.

Daddy was not a good cook, but I enjoyed the lunches he made for us. I liked his fried bologna sandwich with potato chips and a pickle. I loved pickles! We sat and watched cartoons all day until Grandma Lily came home to start dinner.

Every day at five o'clock, he would go sit on the porch and watch Momma walk down the street from the bus stop. By the time she got to the stop sign, he would start walking in the opposite direction toward the park, looking back a few times to make sure she made it into the yard and onto the porch. A minimal amount of interaction to keep some level of peace.

My parents' relationship was awkward. They never spent time together unless they were fighting. I never saw my parents hugging, kissing, or holding hands. They were just "together."

Charlie lacked the communication and attention that Whitney was already used to not getting from her father, Raymond. They say that girls look for their father in a man. She had a point of view of her father but never decided to share it with anyone. Accepting certain behaviors from a man that she grew to love was a subconscious act. She did not want something different. A man saying, "I love you," and showing it in abusive ways was a learned behavior that was acceptable for Whitney Maxwell.

Shortly after my second birthday, Momma had a baby. It was a girl, Karla, and she was now getting all of Momma's sweet, loving attention. I felt a new level of being unwanted and lonely. Karla got picked up and held all the time whenever she cried, and she cried a lot! When I started crying, Momma would just yell at me to shut up, saying, "Girl, ain't nothing wrong with you!" I was used to being ignored but with a new baby, I was ignored more often. I had to play by myself and use my imagination to be somewhere else besides at home.

My mother did not make quality time for me, and Daddy was never home to color or play with me anymore. I only saw him when he was fighting with Momma, eating, or sleeping. The fights were getting worse between them. With two children to look after, Momma was always tired and complaining about everything. She barely combed her hair, and was gaining more and more weight. She stopped going to work and stayed home to watch us all day.

I missed coloring with Daddy. Momma never played with me during the day. I had to play alone. I would watch her take care of Karla, hugging and kissing her throughout the day. I wanted some affection from Momma but no matter what I did, she ignored me, and I did not understand why or what I was doing wrong.

Karla was six months old when Momma went back to work. I was able to start preschool. Every morning, Momma would get me dressed and make oatmeal or cereal for breakfast. We would walk to the end of the street and catch the bus to my school. She would even tell me when to ring the bell for our stop. I enjoyed being at school with other children. My teachers were nice to me. They gave me hugs and praise for doing a good job. The children were loud, but it was a cheerful, happy noise level.

Every day before it got dark, Momma would pick me up. There were very few times that Daddy drove Momma to my school. It was usually raining or snowing, but other than bad weather days, we rode the public bus.

By the time I got home from school, Grandma Lily had already cooked dinner. She was happy to see me and would fix me a plate. I would receive the biggest hug and kisses.

Grandma Lily started picking me up from school twice a week. She always made sure I wore my seat belt. As she drove, we would sing songs together, have secret ice cream dates, and throw pennies into the huge water fountains at the mall. Some days we would go to visit some of her relatives. I always enjoyed my time with Grandma Lily.

The Toys R Us catalog would come in the mail right before Thanksgiving, and Grandma Lily would have me circle everything that I wanted. I circled more than half of the book!

Christmas that year was the worst. I woke up excited to see all the presents under the beautifully decorated tree. Before I could get to the dining room to see what Santa Claus left for me, there was a fight happening in the kitchen. Momma began packing her clothes and throwing my stuff into large, black trash bags. Karla was crying. I was standing in front of the tree, confused, ready to open and enjoy my gifts.

Daddy hit Momma so hard that she called the police and when they arrived, they took Daddy to jail. Momma was crying again. I was not sure if she was crying from their fight or because he was being arrested. It was an emotional mess on Christmas morning. Grandma Lily rushed home from work, and she started yelling at Momma too! I had never seen her upset or heard her yell at Momma. She was angry that Daddy was in jail and told Momma she had to leave her house. Grandma Lily had reached her final straw and had enough of their fighting and toxic relationship.

A few hours later, we left Grandma Lily's house and went to stay with Momma's parents. Papa Ray pulled up and put all of the black garbage bags in the back of his pickup truck and we left. As we drove away I looked out of the back window, waving at Grandma; she waved back and blew me a kiss. I cried silently in the backseat. I had left all of my presents and new toys under the tree. I wanted to stay with Grandma Lily but Momma said I couldn't. Papa was listening to the sports radio turned up loud as he just whistled the whole ride, looking over at his daughter and shaking his head. I could not stop my tears from flowing. I was sad and alone on Christmas.

CHAPTER 4

I did not visit with Grandma Mabel and Papa Ray often as a toddler. I quickly learned just how strict and different their rules were. It was the complete opposite of Grandma Lily. I was restricted from doing most anything. I was not allowed to do or touch anything! No watching TV and sitting on any of the pretty, blue furniture that was covered in thick, clear plastic. The living room was not to be sat in. I was not allowed in the kitchen unless I was sitting at the table to eat a meal. At least Grandma Lily would allow me to watch her cook or wash dishes while I colored at the table. I wanted to go home!

Momma stayed in her room in the attic. Most afternoons I would sit in the hallway, playing with my toys. Nobody talked to me or played with me. I was just there, always all alone.

By the time I turned three, Momma brought home another baby. This time it was a baby boy, Wesley. Now both Karla and Wesley were getting all her attention. Momma ignored me most of the time unless she was telling me to do something. "Go get me a diaper for your sister," or, "Take these dishes downstairs." I was Mommy's big helper.

Mabel Maxwell did not teach Whitney about birth control

before she began having sex. She was taught that Christians did not believe in abortions. Whitney was unmarried and chose to have three babies before she tied her tubes. Without the support of Charlie, and three ungrateful brats to provide for, it was more than enough for her to deal with alone. She wanted to live and enjoy her life.

I did not see Daddy or Grandma Lily for a very long time after we moved out. I was sad, and missed seeing my grandma every day. Momma stopped taking me to school for a few weeks after Wesley was born. I was just stuck in the house all day, every day, with Momma and the crying babies.

Grandma Mabel was always up early in the mornings, cooking breakfast and starting dinner every day before she went to work. She was a great cook, and all of her food was delicious. She was only nice to me when Papa Ray was not home. She would let me mix the bowl while she baked cookies and cakes for her church members. She taught me gospel songs, but dancing was not allowed in her house.

When Papa Ray was home, she was strict, and we all had to follow the rules. I was not allowed to do anything, especially in the kitchen. "Kids don't belong in the kitchen playing over my food," and, "Kids are to be seen and not heard," is what he would say. I did not understand it, but I knew to stay out of his way when he was around the house. Papa Ray would just sit and look at me and shake his head. He was a quiet man that did not say much but you could tell he was thinking about something.

One Wednesday morning, Momma was ironing our clothes so we could get dressed for the day. She placed the hot iron in the bathroom on the shelf. She always said not to touch it, but she never explained why. So, when I went to the bathroom to brush my teeth, I was curious and touched the shiny silver part of the hot iron. I screamed! It was hot, and my entire hand immediately turned red. Momma came running into the bathroom and looked at my hand. "I told yo hardheaded ass not to touch that iron! Girl, look at your hand!" She was angry at me, even as I could feel the burning and throbbing. I cried as I watched my skin melt off my hand. "Go downstairs to breakfast and hush up that noise," she said.

Holding my hand up, I cried silently, as I was not thinking about eating. Wasn't I supposed to get a Band-Aid or something to make my hand feel better? I was emotional and in a lot of pain.

I showed Grandma Mabel my hand as soon as I got downstairs and she asked me what happened. "I touched the hot iron."

I could see her empathy as she grabbed my hand. "Baby, the iron is hot, just like the stove. What did yo momma put on it?"

I shook my head and said, "Nothing."

She told me come over to the sink. Grandma mumbled a few words under her breath as she ran cold water on my now swollen, red hand. I was in so much pain, but my tears had stopped. She took the butter knife and sliced a huge piece of Imperial butter and put it in my hand. "Rub that on your hand, baby," she said. I'd only had butter on my toast and pancakes, it was both weird and made my hand feel better, so I didn't care. It took a few weeks for my hand to fully heal. I had to learn how to color and do everything with my left hand.

I spent the next week with Daddy instead of going to school. Momma did not pick me up until after my hand healed and I was able to use my hand again. Grandma Mabel told her not to take me to school because they might think she did it to me. So, I got dropped off at Grandma Lily's house. I was sad about my hand but happy to finally go home.

Daddy did not work; he stayed home and watched TV with me all day. We watched cartoons, soap operas, and game shows, all day. He would fry me a bologna and cheese sandwich on white toast and give me chips and a cup of red Kool-Aid. Grandma would come home from work by 3:00 p.m. and she would change her clothes, sit down, and read for a few hours every day. She taught me how to read before I started kindergarten. I fell in love with reading books. At 5:00 p.m. we ate dinner and at 7:00 p.m. we watched *Wheel of Fortune*, the lottery numbers, and *Jeopardy*. Momma usually came to pick me up after *Jeopardy* was over.

Eventually, Momma began taking all three of us to Grandma Lily's on the weekends. Karla and Wesley were still babies. Grandma Lily had not seen Wesley yet. The first day back at her house was weird. The smell of the house was the same: cigarettes and food. When we walked through the door, she helped me take my coat off and gave me the biggest hug and kiss. We missed one another and I started crying. "What's wrong, baby?" Grandma Lily asked me.

"Grandma, I wanna live with you again. I really miss being here with you," I told her.

Momma was walking through the door with Wesley in his car seat and saw me wiping my face. “Khloe, what is yo ass crying about now?”

I looked up but before I could respond, Grandma Lily spoke up. “Whitney, leave my grandbaby alone! We will see you tomorrow, I’ll drop them off around seven thirty.” Momma said nothing, just rolled her eyes and walked back out the door. I was thankful that Grandma spoke up for me because explaining that I would rather live with Lily than at the Maxwells was something Momma knew but did not want to hear me say. I was sad inside, and did not know how to express my emotions or what to do with them. I began to feel angry inside and I started resenting Momma.

Momma eventually found a new job working downtown so after a few months, we moved upstairs into a two-family house. I was excited to have bunk beds. The three of us shared a bedroom and Momma had her room. It felt good to not have to sleep on a futon next to the babies. I got the top bunk because Karla was too small to climb up and down the ladder.

CHAPTER 5

Turning five was my most exciting birthday. I was able to start kindergarten. I loved school, and was ready to get away from Momma and the babies all day. Right before Thanksgiving break, one day after school, Momma picked me up instead of my catching the school bus home. She said I had an appointment to take a test at another school. I was nervous, but excited about taking the test.

When I arrived, there were children from other schools with different-colored uniform shirts. They were there to take the test too. We all sat in one classroom, with one teacher. They were nice, but I did not know why I was there besides to take a school test.

One week later, my kindergarten teacher, Mrs. Williams had me and three other students follow her to Ms. Harvey's first-grade class. I was now in the first-grade class after lunch until the end of the day. I was academically advanced enough to learn math and reading.

The teacher started giving me homework right away and at some point, the principal told Momma that I had to go to a different school. I was placed into a Gifted & Talented program. She didn't explain much to me, so I didn't know what was wrong with my current school that I had to transfer to a new one.

The school was across town from where we lived. Other children from other neighborhoods came to this school too. I got excited once I found out that I got to ride the school bus every day. I knew it was going to be a long ride, stopping to pick up and drop off children. One hour and twenty minutes, to be exact. I was one of the first pickups and one of the last to be dropped off.

At home, I was used to being alone but, on the bus and at school, everyone talked to me. All my teachers were nice to me and I felt important at school. There were a few children from my neighborhood that went to the same school and were in my class, but I had to learn how to make new friends. I got in trouble at times for talking too much during class but I was a good student and earned straight As.

The following school year, I transferred to a different elementary school that was closer to home and for Gifted & Talented students only. I rode Bus 749 from the second to the fifth grade.

My years of elementary school allowed me to explore the neighborhood because I had to ride the school bus every day. I walked through the neighborhood early in the morning, sometimes while it was still dark outside. Momma did not get up before us to make us breakfast or pack our lunch. If I wanted a hot breakfast, I had to eat it at school. I hated when the bus was late because we got the peanut butter and jelly on graham crackers and milk. Don't get me wrong, that was a good breakfast too, but I appreciated the hot breakfast to get my day started at school. Once I got to the third grade, I was able to scramble eggs and make toast with a slice of cheese, wrapped in foil, for the three of us before school.

At age eleven, I was focused on my newest passion: cooking. Momma wasn't that good at grocery shopping, so I made meals out of what she kept in the pantry and freezer. I tried new and different recipes. I began tearing recipes from magazines when I went to the salon with Grandma Mabel on Saturdays. I would try to go grocery shopping with Momma so I could pick out stuff I wanted to cook.

She allowed me to cook with her, but she never explained the process of prep or how long it took to cook something. I was comfortable with her silence because I learned by watching and practicing. Show me one time, I can repeat it and master it. Cooking for the holidays was the best. Although I did not care for some of Momma's recipes, she was a good cook. I learned a lot from both Momma and Grandma Mabel in the kitchen.

Keeping my lips moisturized and soft was a personal goal. I had nice, juicy lips and had a pet peeve about dry lips. Momma ordered lip balm from the Avon lady at Mabel's salon. Her favorite was strawberry, so she ordered me and Karla the other flavors besides strawberry. I did not see a big deal in us having the same lip balm, but Momma did not share her favorite.

Once I started middle school, I did most of the cooking. Momma made it known that she was not cooking for anybody on Fridays. She barely cooked during the week, but it was "fend for yourself Friday," which meant we had to check the fridge for leftovers or cook something on our own. There was always a limit on what I could cook and warm up. If something was hers, a Pepsi or leftovers from a restaurant,

Momma was not sharing, and asking her made it worse. "I can't eat horse shit," or, "I can't drink rat piss," always displaying a level of selfishness and never sharing "her" food.

I was a chef in the making, and Karla and Wesley waited for me to create something for us to eat. My favorite dinners to cook were pancakes and sausage or fried bologna and cheese sandwiches with fries. Momma would ask for a plate if she was home and did not feel like fending for herself.

Momma started leaving us in the house alone more the older I got. At first, it was for a few hours, then it grew to be weekends. She called home and checked on us or to give me orders but she was comfortable being gone from home and her children.

Grandma Mabel preferred that Momma left us at her house instead of in the house alone. I think Momma enjoyed spiting Mabel and leaving us home alone. Momma was just too busy chasing her men to spend quality time with us on the weekends.

When I was in the 4th grade, Momma's friend Elaine came to live with us. Elaine was a weird and quiet lady. She moved in because her parents put her out. Momma was nice to her friends, so she opened her doors when she should've kept them closed to the demons of other people. Momma was home a lot less, even a few days at a time, because Elaine was always home with us. She did not know how to drive, so she never went anywhere.

To show her appreciation, Momma began paying her for "babysitting" us while she was away on the weekends. I did not care, I was just glad to have someone be nice to me at home. Elaine stayed with us for a couple of months and once Momma began paying her, she would order pizza for us on Fridays. Elaine did not talk a lot and just watched TV all day. She did our laundry and kept the living room clean.

One day when I came home from school, all of Elaine's stuff was gone from the living room corner and Momma was drinking wine and smoking cigarettes. I could tell that she was mad about something. When Momma's best friend, Robyn, called, that's when I found out what happened. I sat on the stairs out of her sight but close enough to hear her phone conversation. "Girl, that bitch was buying pizza with my muthafuckin' money!" I tried not to laugh as I listened to her tell Robyn how Elaine was using her extra checks out of her panty drawer to order pizza every Friday. It took her over a month to notice what was going on with her bank account. Momma was always gone and did not manage her money well, so she got played and was pissed off about it. "I shoulda whooped her slow ass!" she yelled. I listened to them talk and gossip as she drank her wine. Momma eventually called me downstairs to pour her some more wine and to change the channel on the TV that she was barely watching.

It was not long before Elaine was back at our house. This time, Momma put a lock on her bedroom door, and she was back in the bar with her freedom again. We were back to finding our dinner on Fridays. I was not risking my life to eat anything Elaine cooked, so I had to cook for all four of us. I didn't know her; she was Momma's friend, but she was also a thief and a liar. She was not going to poison me! I was always weird about eating other people's food, especially if they could not be trusted.

Christmas of my 4th-grade year, Daddy called early to say Merry Christmas. Momma was instantly annoyed that he called at 8:00 a.m. Our house phone rang loud, upstairs and downstairs. So, it woke the whole house up. He told me we had gifts at his house.

I was happy to see Grandma Lily. She always made Christmas special for me. She bought things that I liked, but would not have thought about asking for. I asked her to take me shopping instead of her picking out clothes for me. Grandma was not the best at picking out clothes without me.

Grandma Lily picked us up around 3:00 p.m. to take us to her house. We opened gifts from Grandma Lily, and Daddy. Grandma bought me two crochet rugs, sweaters, and journals with gel pens. I was excited to see what Daddy got me. I unwrapped two packs of underwear and two packs of undershirts. The underwear was too small. I looked at him, smiled, and said, "Thank you." He smiled and went into the kitchen. I was thankful that he bought me something. I was upset because I could not fit into it. I didn't know how to tell him, so I didn't say anything. There was no way of him knowing my sizes. He did not buy me anything regularly. He was too stubborn to call Momma, so he took a guess.

Not only were my underwear too small for me, but Karla and Wesley's underwear were also too small for them too. I did not want to be ungrateful, but I was not sure what to do with too small underwear. How do you get rid of a Christmas gift that was intended for you but cannot fit? I was confused.

Grandpa Charlie never asked us what we wanted. He was my Black Santa Claus. He just showed up with big, black trash bags full of toys. Two bags for each of us. Grandpa Charlie always bought us toys and lots of noisemakers. When he came over, he asked Momma for a glass of ice and sipped his drink while we opened our presents and played.

By the time I got to 5th grade, I was the same size as some of the boys in my class and just as strong too. It took one girl to call me a bully for cracking jokes about Destiny's cocked eyes and Janice's stuttering problem. I was labeled a bully by my peers and teachers. I received plenty of after-school detentions. I would beg Miss Freeman not to call my mother. I knew better than to allow a teacher to call Momma at work about my behavior. It was an instant whooping when I got home. No questions asked. Miss Freeman took me seriously enough not to call her but still gave me the detentions. I lied and told Momma that I was staying after school for tutoring. She did not care, because they sent us home on a bus and dropped us off in front of our house.

I got in trouble for talking in class, but I was an Honor Roll student. I enjoyed learning and loved school. Momma was a math whiz. She taught me how to do mental math and solve problems without writing them down. Momma never came to any of my awards ceremonies. Most of the time, they were in the middle of the afternoon and she had to work. I did not feel celebrated for my accomplishments at school. My classmates' parents would bring them flowers and balloons and take them out to lunch. I wanted special treatment too for my awards and good grades.

When she would get home after work, I would be excited to show her my certificates. "Good job, Khloe. The perfect attendance is mine because I send yo ass to school every day," she would say. I worked hard, but that was not enough to satisfy my mother.

Fifth grade was my favorite year of elementary school. I was headed to middle school and ready to not have to wear school uniforms anymore. Mr. Muhammed, my principal, announced during morning announcements that we would be having a Father-Daughter dance. I was not excited, but wanted to go. I took the flyer home and Momma told me to call Daddy and ask him. I did not talk to him often and I was nervous to ask him. I waited until after dinner and called. His tone was always the same. He spoke low and dry. He said yes, he would go, but Momma would have to pick him up and take us because he did not have a car.

Grandma Lily bought me a beautiful, white dress, shoes, and lace socks for the dance. Grandma Mabel made sure that my hair was curled and picture ready. The evening of the dance, I got dressed and we drove to Daddy's house to pick him up. When we got there, he was upset that we were running late. He was sitting on the porch frowning when we pulled up. Momma and Grandma Lily took our picture and we headed toward my school.

Arriving at the school, Momma dropped us off at the door. She told Daddy she would be back at 8:00 p.m. when the dance was over. Walking through the school building at nighttime was weird. Dark classrooms and empty hallways. The school gym was lit up with decorations and lights. There were balloons and flowers at the entrance in the shape of two hearts. Mr. Muhammed spoke to me and shook Daddy's hand. Mr. Muhammed said, "Khloe is an excellent student, I'm sure you're proud of her."

Daddy looked at me and smiled. "I am."

The photographer took our picture and we headed straight to the dance floor. Line dances, break dancing, just having fun. Daddy was not a good dancer, but we had fun. They served us pizza, chips, and cookies. We drank punch with rainbow sherbet on top and ate cupcakes. The DJ had us dancing and sweating until the party was over. I sweated my curls out.

Momma was already waiting for us when we got outside. I had a good time with my dad at the dance. During the car ride home, my parents did not talk to one another. I sat in the backseat observing their body language and energy. They really did not like one another. Momma dropped Daddy off at home and he thanked her for taking us. He kissed me on my forehead and said, "I had fun with you and your friends at the dance. Goodnight, Khloe, I love you."

There was this boy named Austin. We had been classmates since the second grade, and he was an annoying, big-headed boy. He would bother me all the time at lunch and recess. I would ask him to leave me alone, every day. At recess, Austin would follow me around and just mock me. I would walk away, and he would follow me, talking about nothing. I would jump rope and he would jump rope too.

One day when we came outside after lunch, he decided to

chase me. So, I ran as fast as I could until I got tired. When I stopped running, I turned around and slapped him across the face. He started screaming, and the teacher instantly came over to see what happened. I was sent to the principal's office for fighting. But I was not in a fight. I was defending myself. Three days suspended from school and I had to have parent and teacher counseling. I was weeks away from fifth-grade promotion. They had to call Momma and tell her what I did.

When she finally got there, she had this evil look on her face. I think I saw smoke coming out of her ears and horns on the top of her head. She never wanted to hear my side of the story; she just took their word for it. Austin's dad looked like a black Abraham Lincoln. He was extra tall and had a deep voice. He just stared at me with a scolding eye.

The principal and both of our parents had to decide if I was going to walk across the stage with my class or sit out because I had scratched Austin's face from his eye down to his chin. I did not remember scratching him like that. They all wanted me to say that I was sorry. I was confused as to why I should apologize for a slap that he had earned. I wasn't sorry! And when I said that, I made things worse for myself.

"Khloe, I am extremely disappointed in you. You are one of my best students and your behavior is unacceptable," said Principal Muhammad.

All of my friends knew I was tired of him bothering me, so they were proud that I stood up for myself. The boys in my class stopped talking to me and no longer wanted to play with me during recess. I did not care. That became my line and my answer to everything, "I don't care."

I always went to public school. Karla and Wesley were usually in a charter or Catholic school, rarely public schools. We were all very smart, and capable of getting good grades. Momma would tell me that I had to be good in school and set an example for my siblings because I was the oldest. They were not paying me any attention, so I'm not sure who I was setting the example for, but I was sick of the responsibility altogether. I never asked for the job, and now I was responsible for something I did not want. Both were bad in school and always getting into trouble. I was not sure how well I was doing at the good example thing.

Momma had to go to their schools a lot or transfer them in the middle of the year because the principal would tell her that their behavior was too much of a distraction for the school. Not just the classroom, other students, or the teachers, the entire school! One year, Wesley went to three different schools for one grade. He was a problem child at a young age.

CHAPTER 6

When Wesley started school, he had behavior issues. He was full of energy and was very curious and mischievous. All the time, no matter where he went. Momma would beat Wesley, but he was still bad. So, she whooped him for everything. Every mother has different struggles with each child.

Momma allowed her boyfriends to whoop and beat up on Wesley. She said he needed a man in his life to discipline him so whoever she was with had new ideas for discipline. "The Bible says, 'spare the rod, spoil the child,' and I do not plan to spoil none of y'all," Momma would say.

The abuse was not necessary all the time. I was tired of witnessing it. She barely knew these men but thought it was okay for them to smack Wesley around and release their frustrations by beating him. He had a lot of behavior problems. It was not from a lack of discipline. The beatings made Wesley angry. I believe he would act worse after each beating. Momma could not control Wesley and Daddy wanted nothing to do with him.

Wesley was bad at home and even worse at school. He terrorized the students and teachers. He had a sweet, devilish smile and was a busy, mischievous little boy. Mischievous was an understatement. He was always going in Momma's purse and room to take her change. Wesley would steal from the store and did not care if someone saw him or if he got caught. He got immune to the beatings, so trouble followed him no matter the consequences.

Wesley and Karla were always eating something that belonged to her. Something she did not want to share. The two of them would eat it and just take the whooping for it later. This particular beating was about her six-pack of Pepsi she hid behind the eggs in the fridge. She drank two and there was one left.

The next day, Wesley came home from school with a note about the bruises he had on his legs and back. Momma had beat him the night before until his skin broke and was bleeding. The note was from the guidance counselor, stating that CPS (Child Protective Services) would be stopping by our home. That note spooked her good. She went to the grocery store and stocked our cabinets and freezer. It felt like Christmas to have so much food in the house. She even bought our favorite snacks and ice cream treats. When Saturday morning came, she initiated cleaning up the house, which never happened.

The lady from CPS showed up Tuesday evening after Momma got home from work. She wrote notes as she walked through the house. After the lady left, Momma was nice and did not whoop any of us for a while. She started taking parenting and anger management classes. Hopefully, she was learning how to discipline her kids without tearing holes in their skin. I am not sure if the classes helped, but she got a certificate of completion.

Wesley was headed to the fourth grade when Momma got sick of his behavior in school. The whoopings were not enough; he was immune to them, and did not care about punishment. The only thing that bothered Wesley was not being able to go outside on the weekends.

Mr. Carter, Wesley's teacher, was sending home notes and calling Momma every day. His behavior was so bad that year and Momma was fed up. She allowed Mr. Carter to come over and whoop Wesley so he would respect him and sit down in his class. It worked for a week, but then Mr. Carter was back calling Momma, asking permission to whoop Wesley again.

Momma got a referral from Wesley's pediatrician to take him to see a psychiatrist. After they ran numerous tests on him and waited for the results, Momma explained to us what was going on. He was diagnosed with ADHD. But I didn't think anything was wrong with him, he was just bad. "Wesley is going to be getting observed by the doctors and his teachers. He will be taking a different medication for the next four weeks," she said. Wesley did not look too thrilled about the process, but he had no choice.

The first week of medication was weird. Wesley went from talking and playing all the time to being a complete zombie. They changed his medicine and dosage a lot in the beginning. He quickly started behaving better in school and brought his grades up from Ds to Bs. Wesley was on the Merit Roll before the end of the school year.

After school, he did his homework and played quietly until dinnertime. Momma did not give him the pills on the weekends, so he could have a break and feel "normal," as she would say.

Wesley was not okay with taking the pills. He was different, and I did not like seeing him like that. He just was not himself. Wesley would ask to stay up late, like he did not want to go to bed. He began wetting the bed again. Sometimes he would wake me in the middle of the night to help him change his sheets and in the morning, the sheets would be wet again. He told me that he was having scary nightmares. Some nights I stayed up with him while he cried himself back to sleep.

Momma did not whoop him for it as she usually would. She said the doctor gave her a list of side effects for each medication, and bedwetting was listed as a side effect. I did not tell her about the nightmares, Wesley and I kept that a secret. She quickly called the doctor's office to adjust his dosage again because she did not want to clean his "pissy mess" or wash "pissy sheets" every day.

Each of his teachers had to give Momma a behavior report on how he behaved in class for four weeks. She gave the doctor the teachers' report and a report of her observation. The doctor decided on one medication and a good dosage. Momma was more than satisfied with her decision to medicate her son. Wesley eventually learned to cope with being medicated.

CHAPTER 7

I believe Momma would get sick to her stomach the way she looked at me sometimes. The resentment she showed me was meant for my father. She was bitter about their nasty breakup and being stuck with the three of us. She did not have any type of contact with him and if they did talk on the phone, it was usually a short conversation. Daddy would say something to piss her off and she would start yelling. He always just hung up on her. It was painful to see them interact with one another. He was saying fuck you to her and the three of us. I was her daily reminder of how much she hated Charlie Randolph.

I had my own opinions of Momma. In my eyes, she was not my idea of a good mother. She had three children by one man she once loved and now hated.

I felt like Momma wanted me to hate Daddy just as much as she did. She was always talking bad about him. "That nigga is a deadbeat. He ain't helping me with y'all because he upset with me." My parents hated one another, and it showed in how they treated one another throughout my life and how they both treated us. I listened to Momma say, "I try not to talk bad about y'all's daddy. I want y'all to see for yourself that he ain't no good." I loved my daddy and was hurt whenever she did mention him. She did not have anything nice to say about him. No, he was never around or spent time with us, but I loved him, and she resented me for the love that I had for him.

At some point in my adolescent years, I started feeling like I wanted to run away, somewhere far from home. She disapproved of everything I did because it was not exactly her way. Never any special treatment. I was not taught to feel good about my accomplishments or myself as an individual. Whenever she disciplined me, I felt like she was trying to kill me. It was like her legit way of fucking me up and releasing her frustrations from her life onto me.

Momma was teaching me all the wrong things; the underlying lessons of self-hate, and ultimately, how to hate her. I taught myself to accept her physical presence alone, because her emotions were empty and absent. She lacked love in her heart for me, her oldest child, unaware that she could not give me something she didn't have to offer. No hugs or kisses to show me that she cared unconsciously created "Mommy issues" within my spirit and my future. I was hungry for affection from my mother. The lack of affection was the size of a huge, empty hole. It was cold and dry.

From how I felt on the inside and the images in front of me, I learned that love hurts. It was the two people you were born to that were supposed to protect, nurture, and love you that hurt you the most. The word *family* comes with a heavy tag and a load of unspoken expectations. The word *family* came with pain. The level of pain had nothing to do with me but was taught through broken pain. No tears were shed because being weak was not allowed.

I do not remember Momma telling me, "I love you." I did not feel loved by Momma, and only heard it from an absent father full of broken promises and lies. I had no clue what love was or what it meant. I did not know how to receive it or express it healthily. I was taught not to discuss what was wrong and felt uncomfortable asking the questions in my head. "What happens in this house, stays in this house," was Momma's favorite line. It was her way of telling us not to repeat anything that goes on. Especially when it was time to go somewhere or to somebody's house. She didn't want Karla and Wesley telling Grandma and Papa Ray her business. I saw and heard a lot of grown-up conversations, parties, and things that I probably should not have seen. Momma was not discreet about how she lived her personal life.

Comparison started at an early age; Momma was always comparing me to her friends' children. It taught me that love and acceptance was built on performance. I did not feel the love in my heart from either of my parents but mainly Momma, since I saw her every day. Her words and actions never added up. The "Good job, Khloe," and, "I'm proud of you, Khloe" were never heartfelt, just words to my ears. Words that I learned to tune out because they were so vacant when spoken.

We stayed in the hood, so there was always an ice cream truck riding around in the summertime. You could hear the music a couple of blocks away before it made it down our street. No matter how nice we asked, Momma always said no to giving us money for ice cream. I was upset and felt embarrassed at times. Even the poor children on the block got some change to get a popsicle from the truck. "If y'all's Daddy paid child support, then maybe I could afford to give y'all money for the ice cream truck," she would say.

She would go buy ice cream treats from the grocery store but would buy chocolate ice cream treats for herself and get us the colorful popsicles that came in a mesh bag. I did not mind the popsicles, but they were small and went quick between the three of us. I enjoyed chocolate ice cream treats as much as she did, so I would sneak and eat her treats whenever I was home alone after school.

I always saved my birthday money and money Grandma Mabel gave me for my good grades, and report cards. I eventually started going into my hidden sock to buy my own ice cream treats. Then her rule became, if I did not have enough for my siblings, then I could not buy anything for myself. I did not want to spend my money on them all the time, but it felt good to be able to buy all three of us something from the ice cream truck when it came back around. That was one of my proud big sister moments.

CHAPTER 8

Momma struggled in her single motherhood, trying to have a life of her own and raise three children. She felt stuck, and yearned for the support from Daddy. He truly had zero intentions of helping her raise and support their three children. She rotated men in and out during her search for a man and father figure for her children. A man was the missing piece to her and the life she wanted to give her children.

Unknown to them was the foundational damage that both Momma and Daddy were projecting onto their children. Momma had become a part of my parental raising that she hated because she never dealt with what hurt her during her own childhood. She did not have a valid and verbal explanation for her internal anger. She unconsciously transferred her anger onto her children. The lack of love and nurturing outweighed healthy relationships and good examples from both parents.

Since I was born, Momma made me feel like it was my fault that I existed, living through the distinction of being obligated to love and nurture a child.

I always had a conflict between Momma's words and actions. She always told me not to smoke weed, do not drink alcohol, but that was all she did with her friends. It was the only example she showed me. Every day, she drank. Momma was not into leading by example. She told me, "Do as I say and not as I do." That was her way of telling me to mind my business. I hated it, and I never understood how a woman that lacked a basic level of nurturing wanted me to listen to everything she said to do while she displayed the complete opposite. She had no clue that her example made it look like all the right things to do. I craved a good example; the unfortunate part was that she was giving me such a bad example and I was learning all the wrong things to do. Momma's example was not what I wanted to follow and become. I learned early that I wanted to be different when I got grown. I did not want to be anything like my mother.

Momma was a functioning alcoholic. Some of her friends had real drinking problems, but she just drank daily. On the weekends, Momma would drink and party hard all night. I never saw Momma throwing up or acting belligerent because she was drunk. She was quick to cuss somebody out, and I had witnessed her getting violent if she was upset enough.

She was also a faithful cigarette smoker. I hated the smell of cigarettes. Grandma Lily smoked too, and after a while, the smoke made my head hurt. It was such a nasty habit to me. When they went on sale, Momma would buy the large box of boxes and store them in our small freezer. She smoked cigarettes every day.

One day, she could not find her lighter. She handed me a single cigarette and said, "Light this on the stove for me." I wanted to try smoking a cigarette, so I puffed it. Trying not to choke too loudly, I almost threw up in my mouth. When I took her the lit cigarette, she knew that I had taken a hit by the look on my face. "That's what you get for trying to be grown," she said sincerely, never looking up from the show she was watching on TV. I was so annoyed by her comment.

Getting mad and being petty toward Momma was where I thrived best. I learned to get creative with my pettiness. I would do small but major things to get her back. I got mad and threw her ashtrays away. She had so many, and they began to disappear, 2 and 3 at a time. It was hilarious because she thought her friends and their company were taking them. She was pissed and confused that ashtrays kept disappearing. I was responsible for taking the trash out, so I made sure they made it to the trash on Wednesday mornings.

Momma would say things that created insecurities within me and changed the way I viewed myself. We were out shopping for school clothes the first time she said, "Khloe, you are too light to wear red, orange, and yellow." I quickly began disliking those colors and did not pick those colors to wear anymore.

I had a hard time trusting Momma and asking her for help. She was not trustworthy or dependable. Her actions proved that to me multiple times, so I stopped asking and just went without or asked someone else. She always told me not to wait until the last minute to ask for help. Usually, at the last minute, she was not able to do what was requested because she waited until the last minute to change her mind. It taught me to keep my word and not disappoint others because I hated the feeling of being let down.

I kept all my feelings and thoughts to myself. I did not trust anyone with my thoughts or to tell what I was going through or dealing with inside of my head. I was emotionally cold to everyone around me and my level of internal unhappiness was unbearable for me to deal with at times. I was too afraid to kill myself because I didn't know what was going to happen once I was dead. As much as I thought about running away and living on the streets, it was something that I did not want to do either. I was depressed. I felt alone. I had no one to talk to. I learned to hold my thoughts, feelings, and secrets to myself.

Her beatings came with talks and a purpose. She talked during the whoopings. "Didn't—I—tell—yo—ass—not—to—do—this—and—that," every word producing a harder hit. I got beat longer and harder until I shed tears. Then she was done torturing me. "Now get the fuck out of my face before I fuck you up worse." I just stared at her as I walked toward the bathroom. I cried while looking in the mirror. I was angry and hated Momma after every beating. Why would I love her when she did not show me any love? I wanted to be anywhere besides home. I never could think of where to go or who would allow me to stay without telling Momma where I was. I would tell Grandma Lily, but she would only get upset and tell me that she could not stand Whitney.

Momma was always a tall, plus-size woman. Every New Year's she would set a resolution to lose weight by going on a diet and working out. When Momma went on a diet, we all went on a diet. Healthy, smelly, cooked, canned, and weird food. She did not cook food separately for us, we had to eat what she was eating. Sometimes I just went to bed hungry because that was her rule. "You don't like what I cook, drink you some water and take yo ass to bed." It was her meal or no meal. I was not allowed to get a bowl of cereal or ramen noodles. I taught myself to cope with my hunger pains and to just look forward to my bowl of cereal in the morning.

Momma's favorite workout trainer was Billy Blanks. She was in love with him and his Tae Bo workout videos. She ordered all his VHS tapes from the infomercial. We put on jogging pants, a t-shirt, and sneakers. I helped her move the living room furniture so we had space to work out. It was fun at times, but she always found a reason to yell at me about something.

All the dieting and exercise routines were short-lived. Maybe a couple of weeks of working out and then she was onto something new. She was never consistent enough to lose weight and keep it off. This taught me to start new things and when I got bored with it or it got too hard to just quit and move onto something else. Finishing what you start and seeing it through to the end was never Momma's way of getting things done.

Momma was a dreamer. She would come up with some great ideas but that was it. She would not follow through with any of her dreams. She had the ambition to write out her ideas into full business plans, drawings of her ideas, and potential earnings. Momma was smart and talented, but lazy. She was not able to find a starting point to follow through and truly build her business empire. She would research different buildings, draw out floor plans for daycare centers, make calls, and leave it all in a notebook once she got bored or busy with her newest boyfriend.

Momma worked in an office building downtown, sometimes switching from one big building to the next. Always the same type of work, just making new friends and learning new habits. She was quick to make new friends and start doing whatever they were into. No matter what, she worked two jobs. She had a hustling spirit. She sold everything from perfumes and colognes to green tea for weight loss. She sold cell phones and two-way pagers. Some weekends she drove around to barber and hair salons to sell her products and make a profit for the day.

Whether the side hustle was successful or not, she tried them all. When she started selling Amway products, she booked shows and went to people's houses. I tagged along and helped her, but I was not into convincing people to buy and use products. She would work these businesses long enough to order the starter kit, turn a profit, and get some stuff for free. After Momma was done with each business venture, she just piled boxes of products in the attic. Products that she never used. Home-based businesses were something that I did not want to do when I became an adult, and I learned that by the time I was ten.

Christmas was the same every year. Momma bought a live tree and we helped her decorate it. When Christmas morning came, we each had a section or area where our gifts were in the living room. She neatly laid our new clothes on the couch. Momma did not wrap our toys. She did not teach us to believe in Santa Claus. "Ain't no hole in our chimney or a fat white man coming here to deliver presents. I work too hard to buy y'all stuff for Christmas."

Chapter 9

When Saturday mornings came, I just wanted to relax and watch TV. I would wake up early and eat a bowl of cereal while watching cartoons. Once Wesley and Karla got up, I would cook breakfast for the three of us. Momma usually kept eggs and sausage in the fridge because she knew I would cook and feed us.

We lived in a colonial-style house, so it was huge. I called it the Big House. Momma would show me how to clean something once and then that chore became mine. I had the most chores. The expectation was for me to clean up all the time because I was the oldest. Still responsible for setting a good example, I guess.

On the weekends, we were told to clean up and if the house was not clean, then we all got in trouble. I hated whoopings so at first, I just cleaned up everything by myself. Karla and Wesley had a list too, but they did not like to clean. They did not care much about getting a whooping. I was left in charge of telling them what to do.

Momma never helped clean up the house. "That's what I had kids for," she said. Some Saturday mornings, she was working at the nursing home. But she would call to remind us to clean up before she came home, never telling us what time she was coming back.

Cleaning the kitchen took me an hour. I had to wash the dishes, sweep, and take the trash out. Washing dishes was the worst! Momma did not like when I used too much dish soap. "A dab will do ya," she would say. There were always a lot of dishes in the sink, as if Momma used every dish from the cabinets. I needed more than a dab of soap to clean the mountain of dirty dishes. No matter how late it was, I was left to clean the entire kitchen by myself. She allowed me to use the big, yellow gloves because she ran the dishwater so hot. By the time I finished and took the gloves off, my hands were red and wrinkled.

We never had a reliable vacuum cleaner. We always had one, but something was always wrong with it. The Kirby vacuum cleaner needed a bag most of the time. But Momma said they were not in her budget. So, I made myself familiar with sweeping the carpet. It took me forever to sweep the downstairs area, but I had to sweep once a week.

Momma would still be out from the night before but when she got home, she was not happy. Even when the house was completely clean, Momma still found something to yell at me about. I learned that I was not capable of satisfying my mother no matter how good the deeds were.

Momma taught me to iron my clothes and that became my responsibility for everyone, including hers. Every night I would iron all our clothes for the next day. At first, I did not like ironing. Over time, I embraced ironing and taught myself how to master pressing and creasing clothes. Ironing relaxed my mind and challenged me to get every wrinkle out of whatever I was ironing.

Whenever Momma felt like I had done something so bad, which was often, for some reason, she would put me on punishment for weeks at a time. One of my cleaning punishments was bleaching and washing all the baseboards throughout the entire house. It was like whatever she did not want to clean but knew had to get cleaned, she waited until I was on punishment to assign the chore to me. I had to clean all the old food that fell under the cover of the stove. The first time she lifted it and set it on the kitchen table, I wanted to throw up! The food was dried up and there were so many random food droppings and grease buildup. It would take me hours, but I had no other choice but to get it done.

I got smart one time and after I cleaned the stove, I placed foil over the surface to keep it clean. The next time she lifted it for me to clean, she cussed me out for using all her foil. I was trying to work smarter, not harder. Of course, she was petty and threw all the foil away just to prove a point. It pissed me off!

Momma did not like doing laundry. It was too much work running up and down the stairs to the basement. She showed me how to work the washer and dryer and that became my Sunday afternoon chore. I did not mind doing laundry, it was folding clothes and matching socks that I disliked the most. Momma would sit and fold clothes while she watched TV, with a glass of wine and her cigarettes. She would tell me that folding clothes was therapeutic to her. She folded clothes so well that there were not many wrinkles to iron out. If the basket of clothes had been sitting for too long, she would ask me to put them in the dryer for 20 minutes to get the wrinkles out. "Oh, I just love warm clothes from the dryer," she would say as she hugged the warm, clean clothes.

I knew what chores I was responsible for, which was basically the entire house. I often tried to clean up before Momma said something to me about cleaning up. I tried to avoid her yelling at me. Momma still found a reason to get upset with me.

Early one Saturday morning, the three of us were up watching Nickelodeon and eating cereal on the living room floor. I heard a truck backing up, beep, beep, beep. I got up to look out the window and saw a Rent-A-Center truck parked in front of our house. Momma wasn't home from the night before, so I called her before they walked up the driveway to the door.

"Ma, the man from Rent-A-Center is back and knocking on the door. What do you want me to tell him?" I asked.

She breathed heavily into the phone like I was disturbing her sleep. It was after 11:00 a.m., and he was now banging on the door. "Khloe, open the door and give him the phone," she said.

"Who is it?" I yelled behind the locked door.

"It's Rent-A-Center, ma'am," the man said politely. I opened the door and there was a young, tall white boy with acne all over his face and a short, chubby Black man. The Black man was in charge and doing all the talking. "We are here for the stove and refrigerator; you have missed payments for the past four months." I handed him the phone through the screen door and closed it while he talked to Momma.

"Okay, Ms. Maxwell. If not by the close of business today, we will be back tomorrow." He smiled at me and handed me the phone back. I knew Momma had hung up on him by the look on his face. He scribbled on a piece of paper and handed me the pink copy. I closed and locked the door and read the paper that the man gave me. It showed 120 days past due for the stove and refrigerator, with 6 months of payments left to pay the appliances off.

The same two men showed up two months later and Momma was home. She wrote a check, handed it to the man, and slammed the door in his face. I felt bad for the man; he was only doing his job. It was obvious when Momma finally paid them off, because they stopped interrupting our Saturday morning cartoons.

CHAPTER 10

You can call someone your father and still be fatherless.

Father—*a male parent. Provider, protector, compassionate, honorable, generous, and consistent.*

Fathers are unaware of the impact they have on their children. Unaware that broken promises create broken people. The lack of his presence influences the children he should be present for.

I felt like a fatherless child. Charlie was not an active father. I did not know much about him as an individual, like his favorite color or his favorite food. We never traveled anywhere together. He was not like other children's fathers. We did not talk about sports or boys. He did not teach me about money. He did not teach me much of anything. There were very few verbal conversations, with a limited amount of words said between the two of us. His absence and his silence were one.

I was his firstborn daughter; I wanted to feel special. I wanted to feel his love. He was nice to me and always told me that he loved me. I wanted to know what "I love you" meant. He said it, but never showed it. I grew numb to those words from him. They did not have a real meaning or an emotional value. They were just words he repeated to me. He would tell me, "Khloe, make sure you listen to yo momma." I wanted to know why he thought I was going to listen to him.

Charlie shared a lot of his features with me through his strong genes. I got plenty of both good and bad qualities. My light skin complexion and deep dimples matched his. He would smile at me but most of the time, he wore a natural frown.

Not having an active father forced me to gravitate toward the other father figures in my life: Papa Ray, Grandpa Charlie, and Uncle Ray. I tried to create an image of a father I desired in my life instead of an absent one. I craved my father's love and attention. Daddy did not have a consistent, active role in our life at all. Grandma Lily and Grandpa Charlie picked up his slack by being there for us regularly.

Seeing my friends with their dads reminded me of everything I did not have and wanted from my father. I would listen to my friends tell me about their stories and quality time with their dad. I wished my dad did anything besides nothing.

Not having my dad around was unfair. I did not understand why he did not want me. I wanted to spend time with him, but he did not feel the same way, and his actions spoke volumes.

Memories of Daddy were few and far between. I could count on hearing from Daddy on my birthday and all major holidays. He always called and said happy birthday. Sometimes when I got in trouble in school, he would talk to me about listening to my mother and my teachers.

My father was bitter about the relationship and the breakup with Momma. He did not care if he saw me or not.

He was too busy living his own life to be concerned about his daughter. All he knew was that he was paying child support and that was all he had to give. He did not want to help provide for me in any way, so I got the bare minimum. He never gave me his priceless time. No ice cream dates in the summer. No sledding and hot cocoa in the winter.

My father was not willing to put his selfish feelings and ways aside for his daughter. He chose the easy route and quit from the beginning. It was my fault. I wanted and expected too much from him. He was not offering me anything besides heartache. I continued to give him chance after chance to not disappoint me.

The pain he created damaged me. It made me angry at him and sad in my heart. I wanted to tell him how I felt. I tried on numerous occasions, but my words and his reactions did not mix well. I grew to lack respect for my father. The things I needed from him were still missing. He was not aware of the damage he was causing and the hate he was creating inside of me. I had no idea what I needed from him but as I got older, I accepted that I was not going to get anything from him at all.

The first time I expressed my emotions to Daddy, I was in the second grade. I wrote him a letter and told him what I wanted and how I felt. Momma showed me how to address it to him and where to put the stamp on the envelope. I walked to the top of the street and dropped it in the mailbox. He never called me and told me he got my letter. He just called a week later and said, "Khloe, tell ya Momma that she can drop y'all off Friday evening for the weekend. I went out and bought some food." He never addressed me about what I wrote, and I was fine with that. But it was not the last letter he would receive from me.

Daddy would ask why I did not call him more often. I felt like it was his responsibility to call and check up on me. He did not take initiative to be a part of my life but wanted me to call and see how he was doing. I was not interested in the responsibility that he dismissed. I wanted my father to be engaged with my life, not the other way around. So if I did not call him, we did not talk.

My father was unaware that his absence was damaging my image of him. My heart loved him, but my mind desired to hate him. I was angry at him. His absence affected me, and he had no clue. I know what it feels like to not like someone and love them at the same time. It is not a good feeling, especially when the person is expected to love and nurture you.

The older I got, the more my love for him faded away. He was the first man that broke my heart. Daddy was a grown boy and did not want the responsibility of being a father. He did not want to be there for me. He showed zero emotions. He taught me not to give a fuck.

His first lesson was to either love me or leave me alone. He showed me that I did not like the feeling of the in between. I loved Daddy, but I wanted him to pick a side and stay there. I wanted him to choose me, but he was consistent with his choice and it was never about me.

Daddy was consistent in one area. Holidays and celebrations. He showed up at Aunt Penny's and Grandma

Lily's for holidays. He was a proud father in front of his family. He attended school graduations and wanted to take pictures of my accomplishments. My achievements that he had zero input on. He did not support me through life at any other stage. None of my bad days or hard days. He only showed up for the celebrations. I did not appreciate it, and I wished he'd stop coming.

On the weekends when I spent the night, I slept upstairs in Grandma's bed. Daddy would come and go throughout the days I was in the house, but he was too busy for me. He was okay with Grandma taking care of me. He would kiss me on the forehead and say, "I love you, Khloe," and walk back out the door. He was a mystery to me most of the time. He did not ask for us to come over but when Momma dropped us off, he had no choice.

As I got older, whenever I would get enough courage to call and ask him for something, he always rejected me. He would simply tell me, "Khloe, I am paying your mother child support. I don't have any extra money to give you." According to Momma, she could not afford to give me money either because his payments were not that much. She had bills and her habits to support. I felt abandoned in ways my parents could not imagine. I wanted so much more from both of them. I could not depend on either of my parents. I could not trust my parents. The two people I needed the most taught me I could not rely on them. Learning such a trait at an early age will limit how you love and trust others. It was best for me to hold all my emotions inside.

A daughter should not have to beg her father for a relationship.

CHAPTER 11

I was taught that crying was a sign of weakness. I caught on quickly, and learned not to cry when something was wrong or bothering me. Crying did not earn me a hug or cuddle to make me feel like everything was going to be okay. If I was getting whooped for something, I forced myself not to cry about it. I had built up anger toward Momma and my tears were a sign of weakness. I got used to the kids at school and church calling me mean. I stopped defending myself by saying I wasn't mean and instead embraced it. I taught myself not to care what people thought of me.

By the time I turned 11, I was consumed with so much anger and rage. I began fighting to release my frustrations. I fought my siblings. I fought in the neighborhood. I fought at school. I got in trouble at church for pushing a girl out of my face. Fighting felt good to me. The physical release of my anger got me in trouble every time. I didn't care. I was sick of people and the things they decided to say to me. I was nice until someone was not nice to me. Then I got in trouble for reacting and taking it too far.

Uncle Ray would pick me up and take me for a ride. He would tell me how important it was to listen to Momma. I allowed that noise to go in one ear and out the other. He told me he did not want me fighting at school and getting in trouble. "Khloe, you're too smart to keep getting in trouble at school."

He began teaching me about boxing. "Boxers fight with technique and purpose," he explained. "Fight with a purpose, and not your emotions." I began watching boxing matches with him. Papa Ray was a boxer when he was younger and taught Uncle Ray everything he knew. I soon fell in love with the sport. He ordered every fight on Pay Per View and invited his friends over. I watched each match, paying close attention to their movements and techniques. I had dreams of becoming a female boxer. The idea soon faded. The female boxers wore face shields but still ended up with black eyes, broken noses, and swollen lips. I was beautiful, and wanted to keep my face intact.

Momma was nice to us when her friends came around. She would brag about my report cards and have me show them my certificates and awards. Her best friend, Robyn, would give me money for my good grades. She knew I saved my money. Karla and Wesley never kept any money because they were always at the corner store. Momma did not keep snacks in the house so whatever money we had, we bought snacks. We bought pop and big bags of chips to share, cookies, and sweet treats from the neighborhood bakery. There were times when Momma would ask me for my money, even guilting me into giving it to her. I hated handing my money over to Momma. I never got it back, like she would lie and tell me. "Khloe, I will give you this back when I get paid Friday." I lost track and was forced to stop counting Fridays.

A few times she said, "As long as I owe you, you'll never be broke." I did not appreciate it, and saw her as a liar. I had earned my money and wanted to spend it on myself, not give it to her. I began spending a little more on snacks and hiding my money in different places. I quickly went "broke" whenever she asked again. "Momma, I spent it at the bakery when I bought the donuts Sunday."

Momma dealt with plenty of people that lied and stole from her. I hated liars and thieves. It showed me people will take advantage of you when you are nice to them. I did not understand forgiving someone and allowing them to treat you badly again. She'd distance herself but allow certain people to come back and make a fool of her a few more times before she was officially done. She had a few good friends. Momma kept people around for her selfish benefit. She found a way to fall out with her friends frequently. I paid attention to how she treated people and I made mental notes on how I wanted to be treated and how I should treat others.

One Sunday night, Robyn began arguing with Momma. Whatever the original argument was about no longer mattered because it started a real fight. I was sitting on the couch watching a movie and then BOOM! When I walked to the kitchen door, Robyn was sitting on the floor with her nose bleeding. Robyn's boyfriend, Fred, was holding Momma back in the corner next to the fridge and I helped Robyn get off the floor. Momma was yelling and still talking shit. "Come on, bitch! Say that shit again and I'm gon' fuck you up!" Nonstop threats. I had never seen my mother act like that, but it wasn't unexpected. They had been drinking and arguing all day.

Momma told Robyn and Fred to get the fuck out of her

house and as Robyn walked toward the door, she spat on Momma. Fred stopped and just moved out of the way of the best friends. It was on! They started throwing punches at each other and pulling hair. Momma slammed Robyn into the china cabinet, breaking the glass door. There was a quick pause as all the glass fell and shattered to the floor. "GET THE FUCK OUTTA MY HOUSE, ROBYN!" Momma screamed. Momma's face was scratched, and blood was trickling down her cheek. Robyn looked a lot worse, with two black eyes and a bloody nose. Her wig was on the floor, and the little hair she did have was all over her head. Momma had put a real beating on her best friend right in front of me. I just stood there and watched, intrigued by their behavior.

After she slammed the door, she looked dead at me. "Go to your room!" she yelled. Broken glass and dishes were everywhere. Two dining chairs were knocked over, and whatever was on the table was now on the floor. I stepped over everything and went to bed.

When I got up early the next morning, everything was still all over the floor. Momma's room door was open, and she was not home. I knew I had to clean up the mess. It took me three hours to get the downstairs cleaned. By the time Karla and Wesley got up, the house was normal again, as if the fight never happened.

Momma was selfish. She thought about herself first, and we had to deal with it. I did not understand why she was so selfish with her children. Selfish about everything. She made a difference between what was hers and what we could have. She did not like sharing anything.

Momma would order pizza on her stay home and party nights. Of course, she had to feed her friends and their guests. She would order one large pepperoni and one large deluxe, which was only for the adults. I wanted to eat deluxe pizza too! It was my favorite pizza, but she didn't care. She was spiteful, and always refused to share anything with us. I even tried asking in front of her friends because that's when she was nice, and I still got a solid no. Not willing to share one slice. She made a difference in what was hers and ours—the kids' stuff. She would buy us the gallon fruit punch and buy the pink lemonade for herself. Sharing was simply out of the question. It was petty to me, and I hated pettiness! She was selfish about everything, especially food. I used to have thoughts about poisoning her food, just to see if she would need me to help save her. I knew if she survived that she would kill me, so I opted against the poison.

As I got older, I saw pictures of birthday parties from when I was younger that I did not remember. Every year I wanted my birthday to be a big deal. I wanted to feel celebrated on my birthday. Open lots of gifts and enjoy the day. Birthdays did not feel special to me growing up.

Momma usually baked a yellow cake with chocolate icing and bought Neapolitan ice cream. She never asked me what kind of cake I wanted. I got what she gave me, and I was grateful.

The first birthday party I remembered was my 12th birthday. Momma cooked spaghetti and fried wingdings, and baked her annual cake, even writing my name in pink icing. Grandma Lily made my day. She bought me a TV for my bedroom. Some of the children from the neighborhood came to sing "Happy Birthday" and eat cake and ice cream. I blew out the candles and wished for a red velvet cake next year.

Daddy called to wish me a happy birthday, but it only made me sad. To be sad on your birthday is the worst feeling ever!

I was not a fan of going to school on my birthday, but I made the best of it. I would ask Grandma Mabel to do my hair the day before. No matter how I asked her to do my hair, she did it how she wanted to do it. When I got home, I tried to fix my hair how I wanted it to look. At school, my teachers and classmates would sing happy birthday to me. Uncle Ray always bought me lunch on my birthday.

We didn't have cable, but I had the basic channels. Channel 32, The Box, played music videos all day. I had to turn my TV off at a certain time during the week. On the weekends I would watch TV all night until I fell asleep. Momma changed that too, once she said her light bill was going up.

I was curious and full of questions. I would ask Momma questions and she would tell me to get the encyclopedia and look it up. Get the dictionary to find the meaning of a word. I enjoyed reading, so I did the next best thing. I went and signed up for a library card. I was excited to go to the library and just read. I would sit in the library for hours after school, reading and learning about everything.

When going to the library became something that I wanted to do more often, it became something we all had to do. I was okay with Karla and Wesley coming to the library with me, but

I did not want to have to babysit. Momma started dropping us off at the library when she needed a few hours to herself. Most of the time, she would come back right before the library closed. Other times, she would give me money so we could catch the bus home before it got too late and dark. I did not mind riding the public bus. I enjoyed looking at the different people and wondering where they were going.

I did not like being the oldest. I always wished that I had a big brother. Karla and Wesley were only a year apart, so they were closer to one another. Karla was an annoying little sister that was a crybaby about every little thing, just to see me get in trouble. Wesley was a cool little brother but very mischievous and ate up all the snacks. He listened to me sometimes and was curious about everything. I tortured them both every time Momma left us home alone.

Momma would tell them, "Khloe is in charge, so listen to what she tells you to do." They still would not listen to me. I would lock them in the toy room in the basement with all the lights off until they screamed and cried. I got a kick out of torturing them for all the times they got me in trouble when Momma was home. My torture got worse the more they got me in trouble. They knew Momma was going to leave us alone again. They had to decide to help me clean up or get tortured. It was blackmail, but it worked.

Karla and I shared a room since I was in kindergarten, so we were always arguing. She never wanted to clean her side of the room. Karla was messy. She left her clothes everywhere and did not put her things away. I was always annoyed with her. Her definition of cleaning up the room meant stuffing everything off the floor under her bed or in the closet. Everything belonged somewhere, and I was the only one that wanted to keep a clean room. I would get revenge. I would clean the entire room and I throw away her toys, and sometimes her clothes.

Any time Karla and I were arguing and fighting, everything was always my fault. Momma would come to see what I had done to my little sister. "I'm sick of y'all always fighting and arguing all the time." Our beatings began to turn into torture.

I was eight years old the first time Momma tied Karla and me up to whoop us. She picked us up from the babysitter's after school with an attitude and getting home, she was upset about something. We were arguing back and forth about something for too long and Momma was fed up. Karla never cleaned up her mess and I refused to get in trouble because she would not clean up after herself. I was tired of taking a whooping for something I did not do. Karla yelled loudly, "Stop!" for the tenth time, and we instantly got called into the living room.

Momma looked pissed off and was silently sitting on the couch. On the coffee table was a glass of wine and she was folding laundry. It was weird, because the TV was not even on. We stood there as she got up and grabbed a few pairs of her nude nylon stockings from a stack that she had already folded. "Lay on the floor facing one another," she said sternly. I was very confused about the instructions, so she kicked the back of my knee and I fell to the floor, hard. "Lay on the floor facing your sister! I'm so sick of y'all fighting all the muthafuckin' time!" she screamed. She tied my hands and Karla's hands together with one pair of stockings. She used another pair to tie our feet together tightly. Our faces were so close, we were nose to nose. We could not move if we wanted to. I kept my eyes closed because I did not want to look at Karla.

Momma went to her bedroom and grabbed her belt. I could hear the buckle as she walked down the short hallway. She began to beat us. We both cried and screamed! She did not care about how much noise we made. "I'm—sick—of—y'all—fighting—all—the—fuckin'—time!" Every word produced a harder hit. She beat both of our asses as we rolled around the living room floor. On our sides, rolling over on top of one another, just rolling back and forth. Both of us attempted to dodge hits. She did not stop swinging and hitting us until she was tired and out of breath.

When she stopped, it felt like my skin was peeling off my back, butt, and legs. Out of breath, she picked up her glass and drank it until it was empty. Still sobbing, I watched Momma step over us, refill her wine glass, and she went back to folding clothes. I just lay on the floor with hate in my eyes as tears rolled down my face, staring at my little sister and feeling her tears and snot on my face. I hated them both! I had done nothing wrong.

Karla begged to get up to go to the bathroom. "If you piss on my floor, I'm gon' beat yo ass again!" she said, not even looking in our direction.

She left us tied up together for what seemed like hours until it was time for her to go to bed. I did not feel her touch when she untied us. I just remember being able to move my arms and legs again. My butt was sore, and I had welts all over the back of my body. I stood in the shower, running the warm water over my sore, red skin. I was in so much pain! I cried during my shower. I cried myself to sleep. I was hurt and angry. The hate I had for Momma and Karla that night was unsettling throughout my body.

The next morning, Momma had already written a note for my teacher saying that I was not allowed to participate in gym class for the rest of the week. Karla and I both had to wear pants and long-sleeve shirts. She told me if I showed anyone at school my bruises, they would take us away from her. She threatened us with Child Protective Services placing us in foster care to keep us quiet. "What happens at home, stays at home." So, I kept my beatings a secret. I wanted to tell my teacher that I was in pain from sitting down all day or tell my friends the truth when they asked why I could not participate in gym class. Internally, I was deeply saddened by my home life.

I wanted to run away. I wanted to not get on the school bus after school. I was eight years old the first time I planned to run away. I wrote it in the back of my homework journal. I was going to get a quarter and get a shopping cart from Sav A Lot grocery store. I was going to hide it behind the garage and put all my stuff in it. I was going to run away and never come back. I had $42 saved in my sock under my jeans in my bottom drawer. I still planned to go to school so I could eat and shower. But I was choosing to live on the streets instead of with Momma. I was sick of her beating me for being the oldest and the example.

When I was ten, our heat got shut off. It was January, snowing, and 20 degrees outside. I overheard Momma on the phone with the gas company and her gas bill was over $5,000. Momma was too proud to ask Grandma and Papa Ray for help, so we had to suffer and freeze. Momma told us to sleep in long johns, sweatsuits and two pairs of socks. We each had two comforters to sleep under.

The first night, it was so hard to fall asleep. I wrapped myself under the comforters so no air could get in, but the big house was so cold. We all slept close to one another on the living room floor to try to keep warm. Each window downstairs was covered in plastic because the windows were so old, and the plastic kept the wind out.

In the morning, Momma set up her four crockpots on the bathroom counter and she filled them with water to heat up. Once the water was hot, I stopped the sink up and added a little cold water so I could wash up. We could not take showers for a week.

Ms. Tracy was our neighbor from across the street. She was Momma's age but did not have any children. Her home was always neat and clean. It smelled weird since she burned sage and incense all day. She had plants situated throughout her living room and each one of them had a name. I admired her African garments and the Black art she had hanging on the walls.

Ms. Tracy was a sweet lady and allowed us to stay at her house after school so we were not in the cold all evening. When Momma got home from work, she cooked dinner at Ms. Tracy's house. We stayed over there until it was time to get ready for bed. I did not want to go home. "Momma, can we please stay here tonight?" I asked. Momma gave me her scolding eye and I knew her answer was no. She was embarrassed, but Ms. Tracy made all of us feel welcome and comfortable.

Mr. Kingston was one of Momma's older friends that she kept around. She could call on him for anything and he would do whatever she asked. Their friendship and relationship was a secret because he was married. Mr. Kingston was a businessman, and had even helped Momma with the down payment on her house and the purchase of her van. He adored Momma, but they could not truly be together. A week and a half later, Mr. Kingston came over and called the gas company. He paid the bill and said, "Whitney, don't have these kids sleeping in this cold house ever again. You waited too long to ask for my help, girl."

I was so happy when the heat came rushing through the vent. I sat in front of the vent with my blanket until I started sweating.

CHAPTER 12

Grandma Lily was a smart woman but did not graduate high school. At 17, she had to start working to help her mother pay the bills. She started her first and only job at the local hospital and advanced through different departments as she gained more experience. She met and married Grandpa Charlie in her early 20s. She was a light-skinned petite woman with moles and soft, black hair. Her moles were all around her eyes and small freckles were scattered on her cheeks. I admired her blue mole the most. When I was younger, I would trace them with my small fingers as we lay in bed together. Being curious, I asked her if I could grow them too. She would laugh, smile, and tell me yes as she kissed me on my forehead.

I wanted to live with Grandma Lily, but I learned to appreciate our weekends together. Grandma woke up early, made her coffee, and cooked breakfast. Grandma Lily wasn't the best cook, but I liked her food. She cooked three meals every day, we ate snacks, and there was always some kind of cake or pie for dessert.

I was the oldest grandchild and Lily's favorite. She would whisper in my ear when it was just the two of us. "Khloe, you're my favorite, sweet girl in the whole world." She allowed me to stay up late and watch whatever I wanted on

TV. I slept in and appreciated the break from being at home. The rules were different, and I missed the days we lived with her.

Grandma Lily's favorite shows were cop shows and old black-and-white romance movies. We took naps in the recliner together. I watched crime shows with Grandma Lily and I wanted to become a lawyer. Grandma Lily said I would be a good lawyer because I asked a lot of questions and I thought about the right questions to ask. Criminals did stupid things and paid their lawyers good to stay out of jail. I wanted to make a lot of money.

I dreaded Sunday evenings when Momma came to pick us up. One Sunday I asked Momma about staying or living with Grandma, and she got mad and yelled at me. "You have to live with me, Khloe, so stop fuckin' asking me because the answer is no!" I learned to keep my thoughts to myself, and tried to spend as many weekends over there as possible.

In the summertime, we got dropped off at Lily's with a big bag of clothes and grocery bags of food. We were staying for the weekend, but that turned into a couple of weeks. I was happy to be at Lily's, but Momma didn't even call to check on us or to say when she was coming back. Grandma Lily took us to the store for snacks and more food. Momma did not send enough and at Grandma's, we were never hungry.

Grandma Lily taught me, "Early is on time. You don't have to rush when you're early." She was more at peace with life and God. She did not attend church regularly, but had strong beliefs and values in God. She attended church sometimes when I invited her to different events. Lily taught me how to pray and have faith in God. She displayed and maintained peace in her home. She would put you out in the nicest way, but you respected it. Lily would remove anyone that disrupted her peace.

Aunt Penny, Grandma Lily's older sister, hosted Thanksgiving dinner at her house. I asked Momma if we could go and the first year, she took us. After we ate dinner, Daddy and his new girlfriend, Teresa, showed up. Suddenly, Momma was ready to go home and left early. My parents could not stomach being around one another, not even for a holiday dinner. Grandma Lily wanted us to stay so she volunteered to take us home later. After that, Grandma took us annually so we could see our cousins and get to know her side of the family.

CHAPTER 13

I watched how Momma swapped men in and out of her life. She disrespected the ones she married and claimed to love. Momma kept her a new boyfriend. As I got older, I paid more attention to the different men that came around. She kept bouncing from one man to the next. They all looked different, dressed different, and some even smelled weird. All the men had some type of issue. Baby momma drama, a wife, jobless, or some form of homelessness, like he was living with a family member before moving in with us. There was never more than a few months where it was just her and the three of us. She did not like being alone, and kept a man close by at all times. She was showing me not to be alone as a woman; keep you a man no matter the cost or the headache. Some of the worst lessons and examples for a young girl to learn. I had no choice but to consistently pay attention to my environment. I was witnessing both good and bad lessons without being able to decipher the two at times.

Most days after work, Momma would go straight to the neighborhood bar when she got off the bus. At first, I thought she worked there as a second job, but she was drinking and hanging out. She would call home to give me detailed instructions on how to prepare dinner so we didn't have to wait on her to eat. I was eleven when I started cooking dinner during the week. She told me that if we needed something, I could call the bar phone. I called a few times. But no matter what I was calling for, she never rushed home. I made the mistake of asking her what time she was coming home. She spoke close to the speaker because the music was loud in the bar. "Khloe, I'm grown. I don't answer to my children." I received the message, and stopped calling the bar. I figured it out and we made do without her, cleaning up and going to bed before she came home.

A few days a week I just saw her the next morning when I was getting up for school. She did not talk to us about anything and we did not ask questions. She started bringing the broke, stinking niggas home from the bars. Some men I saw, some men I only heard from the other side of her bedroom door. I heard and saw a lot of things that I did not understand. Privacy was not private. Momma's favorite line was, "I pay all the bills, and this is my damn house." She "paid the cost to be the boss," and blah blah blah. All the time.

Everything Momma wanted to do, she did, and did not apologize for it because it was "her house, her rules, her way." "Khloe if you don't like my rules in my house then you can leave." I was stuck, and angry! I cried myself to sleep a lot of nights. I wanted to run away. I hated living with Momma. Daddy never wanted to spend time with me or come to pick me up on the weekend.

One evening after work, she came home in a good mood. She turned on music and began cooking dinner and cleaning up. She lit candles and had the house smelling good. This wasn't her usual behavior on a Wednesday, so I knew someone was coming over. Before the food was ready, there was a knock at the front door.

Momma opened the door and a tall shadow was standing there. I saw his smile before he walked through the door. Momma greeted him with a big hug and smile. She introduced him to us as he sat down at our small dining table. I just sat there and looked at him. He was exceptionally good-looking. Coffee-dark skin with muscles, nice teeth, and he smelled amazing. He ate dinner with us. Momma made lasagna, salad, garlic bread, and grape Kool-Aid. Momma was nice and sweet to all of us that night in front of her guy friend.

After dinner, I cleaned the kitchen and went to bed. I knew he slept over because I could hear noises coming from her bedroom. I felt like it took forever to fall asleep.

The next morning, I was coming out of the bathroom when her bedroom door opened. He headed down the stairs and looked back at me. "It was nice meeting you, baby girl," he said, flashing his white smile. He exited out the front door and I never saw that man again.

Chapter 14

I remember the first time Momma brought Stan home. He was the worst! They dated for a few weeks, and one day I heard Momma on the phone saying she was in love. Whatever that meant. He soon moved his clothes in. Stan was tall and had bad skin. His left eye was delayed, so most of the time he looked cross-eyed. I just avoided eye contact with him. I cracked so many jokes about his eyes to Karla and Wesley. Every time we saw him, we just started laughing.

He moved in and started trying to tell us what to do like he was our daddy. We had a daddy, so listening to him was out of the question. The three of us got together and refused to listen to anything he said. No respect for clowns!

One day, Momma sat us down and told us that she was going to marry Stan. "Ugh! Why?" I blurted out, right before she slapped me in my mouth. He did not have a job, he had a bad body odor, and didn't clean up after himself. She said she was in love, blah, blah, blah. I was not interested in anything she had to say after that. I truly did not care. My opinions did not matter to Momma. At some point, they were even discussing having a baby together.

On the morning of the wedding, everything went wrong. Standing in the house of God and 99 percent of things were going wrong, from Wesley's shoes being too small to the groom and groomsmen being late from partying the night before. Whitney had brought her wedding gown to be fitted three months before but was having trouble fitting into it. The wedding was a disaster! She married Stan and changed her last name to his, Elkinson.

Everyone was happy about them getting married and I did not understand why. They canceled their honeymoon plans because they were over budget for the wedding. Papa Ray was already complaining about the amount of money he was spending without any help from the groom. Momma didn't tell her parents the truth about Stan, so they didn't know that he was broke. She only displayed her "happiness" around them, and that was enough for them to pitch in on her big day.

Papa Ray and Grandma Mabel paid for the reception as their wedding present. The wedding was at the church, but the reception was in our backyard at the big house. There were only two things that I enjoyed the whole day. The wedding cake, and helping Momma open all the gifts and cards filled with money. Momma hired a caterer to cook the food. They rented tables, a tent, and chairs. Momma hired the DJ from the bar to play music. Everyone was eating, dancing, and socializing throughout the afternoon.

Papa Ray ate dinner with the wedding party and then disappeared. When I saw him again, he was sitting in a chair, leaned up against the gate. He would fall asleep anywhere. I thought he had a sleeping disorder. I sat under the tent at the table and watched everyone. When I looked at him again, his eyes were closed, and his chin was resting on his chest.

Robyn's mother was sitting next to him, observing the party too. She did not talk that much or walk on her own. Papa Ray was relaxed and napping so good that his head nodded one too many times. He fell out of his chair and hit the ground! He looked up as if someone had pushed him. He jumped up quickly. It all happened so fast that no one else noticed it. It was the funniest thing to watch. He fixed the chair as if it had dropped him. He stood up and dusted the debris off his suit. He leaned toward Robyn's mother and asked her if she was okay. He was the one that fell out of the chair but wanted to know if she was okay. She looked so confused as she nodded her head yes.

I was unhappy with Momma's new relationship. She let Stan take her car whenever he asked. He did not work, so she was still paying all of the bills and now giving him money too. They drank together on the weekends and went out to the bar on date nights. He was belligerent when he was drunk, and that is when they would argue. I could hear the doors slamming, heavy footsteps, and loud voices as I lay awake in bed. Every day they argued about money and him not having a job or helping with the bills. Stan's mother did not care for Momma or the fact that she came with three children. So, they argued about his mother too.

Stan began to yell at us. It was like he was trying to be our daddy soon after the wedding. He always wanted somebody to clean up his mess; he was so lazy. He stayed home all day playing video games while we were at school. Momma would talk to him about getting a job, but he was comfortable with her paying all of the bills. I knew he wasn't right for Momma, but she was just happy to talk to her friends about having a "husband." My husband this, and my husband that. It got old, quickly.

One day I heard her on the phone talking to her best friend, Robyn, about how she had found out that Stan used to smoke water (embalming fluid) a few years before they met. She knew that he used to sell it, but when he relapsed and started smoking it again, she said he would act crazy. Stuff started coming up missing in the house and he would leave with her car all night, not coming home until the next morning.

"Girl, his sex was already boring, and he can barely get it up. I ain't got time for his lazy bullshit no more," she said. A few weeks later, she put Stan out. She signed the divorce papers and changed her last name back to Maxwell. I was happy he was gone, but Momma turned back to her old habits and started staying out all night again. It was the rotation of a vicious cycle.

CHAPTER 15

Not long after Stan left, Momma was back hanging out in the bar every night. After work, a few nights a week, and on Saturday nights. She would hang out with Robyn and Ms. Tracy, our neighbor. They would meet men and when the bar closed, they walked down the street to hang out at our house. Momma partied with her friends into the early morning hours, smoking weed and cigarettes, drinking, and listening to slow jams.

One Friday night, I was lying on the couch watching *Major Payne* when Momma came home. She said I could stay in the living room as they walked through the front room to the kitchen. I could hear parts of their conversations as they laughed and talked about the people in the bar. Ms. Tracy's guy friend, Larry, said he was going to hook Momma up with his friend. Larry and Tracy gave Momma all the details about Dave.

Within a month, she met Dave and brought him home. He was a short, muscular, dark-skinned man. He had a nice smile—and smoked a lot of weed. Dave stayed over one night and he never left, moving right in. Dave was nice to us, and Momma allowed him to tell us what to do. He spoke sternly when passing out chores. We listened to him, unlike Stan. He was always telling us how we should respect Momma, listen to her, and learn from her. I did not want to be anything like her, but I listened to her so I wouldn't get beat. Dave was the type of man that I wanted my father to be like. He was smart, strong, and was nice to us.

The school year of third grade was coming to an end and it was the first time Dave's five children came to stay with us for the summer. It got crowded at times, but we had fun together. There were eight children to cook for, so Momma cooked spaghetti and fried chicken every other week. She had to cook a lot of food for every meal. When she got tired of cooking, she ordered a bunch of $5 pizzas for us.

The eight of us got along like real siblings. Karla and Wesley played with the younger children, and all four of his teenagers were older than me. By age, I was in the middle of everyone. I was happy to have older siblings for a change. I did not have to be the responsible big sister when they were around. They helped with chores and keeping the house clean. I enjoyed hanging out with them. I felt understood and accepted. They listened to me, and gave me advice about school.

Momma and Dave stayed together for two years. At times they went on dates, laughed together, and they were lovey-dovey in front of us. Other times they would yell and argue, slam doors and storm off. Their relationship was long and toxic. By the time I was headed into the fourth grade, Dave slowly started coming home less often. The first time, he went missing for two days. All her calls kept going straight to voicemail and she was worried enough to call all the hospitals and the county jail. Dave showed up a few days later and Momma was pissed off! He fed her a bunch of lies, they argued, and made up. Momma was back being nice to us because Dave was home. In his absence, she was mean to us. She hated being alone with us and her actions showed her emotions.

One night the house phone rang, and I answered. It was Grace, the bartender, calling Momma. I handed her the phone and watched her face while she listened to what Grace was telling her. I could tell she was getting upset as she hung up the phone and rushed out the door. "I'm going to the bar and will be right back," she said. She usually drove up to the bar, but this time, she walked.

When she came back, I heard the side door slam. She came upstairs and slammed her bedroom door shut. She was upset, and stayed in her room with a bottle of wine all night. We still had not seen Dave and when I heard her crying, I knew she was sad about him.

After about two weeks, Dave did not come back, and all of his clothes were gone. Momma seemed to have been okay with his absence and their breakup.

One day, I came home from riding my bike and heard Momma on the phone mentioning Mr. Kingston. We did not see Mr. Kingston often but when he was around, it was short visits. He was a nice man, but he was a mystery to me. He was older, more mature and different from the other men Momma dated. Whenever Mr. Kingston was around, Momma was nice to us.

Mr. Kingston had been away in prison and when he was released, he reached out to Momma. She told me that he was going to stay a few nights so I had to clean up the house while she went downtown to pick him up from the county jail. Not being able to ask too many questions, I had to rely on ear hustling on her phone calls. I was able to put the story together based on what she told me to do and what I heard during her conversations.

Karla and Wesley were already in bed and I was washing the dinner dishes when she came home. I watched everything from the kitchen window. She hit the remote and backed her van into the open garage. She and Mr. Kingston got out, holding hands as they walked toward the house. Mr. Kingston was Jamaican, very tall, and had a strong accent. He was wearing a white t-shirt and boxer shorts. He looked mean until he smiled at Momma. The huge pine tree in our backyard was the halfway point from the garage to the house. Mr. Kingston turned around first and noticed the shadow behind them. The shadow stepped into the light and it was Dave. I couldn't see where he came from, but he was walking out of the garage toward them. Momma started cursing and shouting at Dave. They began arguing and yelling back and forth. Mr. Kinston was a lot taller than Dave so when he stepped between the two of them, the argument ended. I saw his mouth moving but I did not hear what he said to Dave. He grabbed Momma's arm and they walked to the side door. I could hear his deep voice, "Whit, pull it together. Everything's going to be fine. I will take care of Dave." She was still crying, talking about how he left her for the lady around the corner but wanted to sit in the garage waiting for her to come home. They walked in and Mr. Kingston said hi to me and asked me to get Momma a glass of water.

When I closed the fridge, she yelled, "Call the police!" As I ran to the living room to grab the house phone, I saw a fire in our backyard. Dave had set the garage on fire! With the huge tree in the backyard, I just knew that we were all going to die.

I rushed upstairs to wake up Karla and Wesley to get dressed to go to Ms. Tracy's house. I was so scared the house was going to burn down any minute, so I packed some of the things that I wanted to keep in my school bookbag. We ran out the front door and there were two fire trucks and six police cars in front of our house. The smoke had filled the street up and all our neighbors were outside, looking to see what was going on. The firemen escorted us out of the yard as more firefighters ran into our backyard. I turned to look back and saw the garage was burning and melting to the ground. Momma's van was still on fire. Mr. Kingston and Momma were standing in the driveway talking to police officers. Ms. Tracy told Momma we could go to her house and she walked us across the street. Her house was nice and neat, but I wanted to be at home. I just sat on the couch looking out the window. I was sad inside. It was draining to see Momma constantly deal with drama all the time. I wanted everything to be normal, but I did not know what normal was.

CHAPTER 16

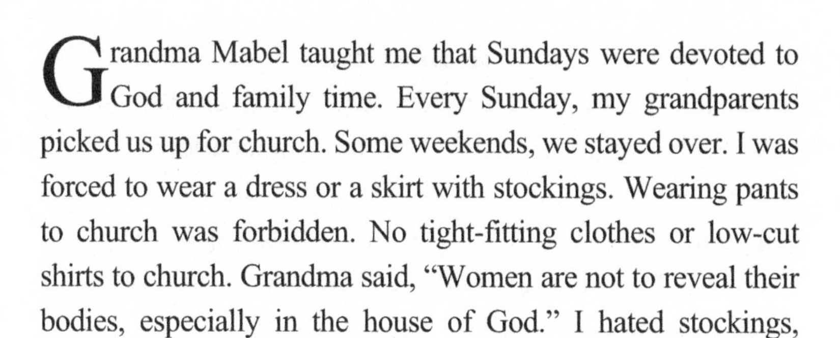

Grandma Mabel taught me that Sundays were devoted to God and family time. Every Sunday, my grandparents picked us up for church. Some weekends, we stayed over. I was forced to wear a dress or a skirt with stockings. Wearing pants to church was forbidden. No tight-fitting clothes or low-cut shirts to church. Grandma said, "Women are not to reveal their bodies, especially in the house of God." I hated stockings, especially during the summer.

For Grandma Mabel, Sunday mornings started at 5:00 a.m. She got up and started breakfast and dinner for the day. She had her 6:00 a.m. morning prayer call before we ate breakfast together at the kitchen table. The goal was to get to Sunday school, but most Sundays we were fashionably late to church, except Papa. He left everyone at home so he could get to church on time and start devotion. Grandma was late all the time, no matter where she had to go. Grandma was busy ironing clothes, washing dishes, preparing dinner, and still in need of getting herself dressed and out the door.

Sunday school started at 9:30 a.m. and Morning Worship Service at 11:00 a.m. At least two out of four Sundays a month, there was a special day to celebrate at church. Pastor Anniversary, Church Anniversary, Usher Board Committee, or evening Revival. The mothers and deaconess board would prepare and serve dinner by 4:00 p.m. I was not a fan of eating everyone's cooking. Most of the time, Grandma Mabel cooked a few dishes and made a dessert. If the food did not look right and smell good, I was not eating it. I wasn't a picky eater; I just did not like to eat everyone's cooking. We lived across town from the church, so we stayed, and I either had to eat something or be hungry.

On Wednesdays, it was Bible study. Thursday was choir rehearsals. Every third Saturday was youth church for the kids. Kid's church consisted of the grandchildren of the church members and some of the kids from the neighborhood. We sat in the sanctuary listening to the youth pastor teach us the books of the Bible. We learned how to make the right decisions by listening to God

and following the Ten Commandments. I enjoyed going to church and learning about God. I took notes when the pastor was preaching, and I studied Bible scriptures.

For a long time, we only celebrated Halloween at church. Momma taught us Halloween was the devil's holiday. Grandma Mabel said, "It's not Christ-like to dress up in demonic costumes and ring folks' doorbells begging for candy." So, we went to church on Halloween without costumes. Every year the youth committee would set up a Holy Carnival in the fellowship hall in the basement of the church. We bobbed for apples, had donut-eating contests, and guessed how many candy corns were in the jar. Grandma Mabel baked cookies and Pastor Buford ordered pizzas. When the carnival was over, they passed out big bags of candy.

As we were returning home with our candy bags, Momma

just shook her head. "Y'all ain't about to sit up here and eat all this damn candy," she said. She dumped all three bags on the table and had us sort and separate the candy into piles. She picked through and took the chocolate candy bars she wanted. As she stuffed a fun-size Snickers in her mouth she said, "Y'all can have two pieces a day until it's gone." I was upset! I did not even want candy anymore. It was petty of her not to allow us to eat our Halloween candy. Every day after school we asked for candy and she allowed us to look through the bag and take a couple of pieces. I took more than two, but the candy bag was disappearing quicker than our two pieces per day. Within a few weeks, I was done asking for Halloween candy. It was a pointless holiday, and I did not care that we didn't celebrate Halloween.

Every month the church was raising money for the building fund. They sold dinners, had car washes in the summer, and collected extra offerings during services for the roof repairs and new wheelchair ramp. The fundraisers were never-ending, and I was not sure if something was wrong with the roof or if it was ever going to get repaired.

Our church was full of gossip. Everybody talked about one another. Grandma Mabel talked about everybody too! Her friends, church members, clients, and family. Nobody was off-limits to being judged by the perfect Sister Mabel Maxwell. You knew everybody's business because everybody was spreading gossip. I used to look around during church service and wonder who was going to heaven. I had heard some of the things the church folks were doing when they were not at church. I knew it was not my place to judge but as a kid, I was curious as to how it worked. I knew I wanted to go to heaven.

Grandma Mabel told us that we had to join one of the committees. I did not want to sing in the choir. I could not sing! I knew my strengths and weaknesses, and singing was my weakness. I did not want to be an usher, so I chose to read the announcements once a month. I did not like getting up in front of the congregation to do anything, but I did not have much of an option to say no. That was not enough for Grandma Mabel, so she forced me to sing in the choir with the rest of the kids. She said, "Your Momma, Samantha, and Ray Jr. sang in the children's choir when they were little, and I want y'all to do the same."

Momma showed up at church sometimes; not as often as Grandma wanted her to. She mainly showed up if the children's choir was singing or one of us was performing in a play. Karla was a praise dancer and they danced on the same Sunday the children's choir sang. After service, Momma pinched me for not moving my mouth during the songs.

The choir director, Sister Baxter, was a short, dark-skinned, mean old lady. Sister Baxter had thick eyeglasses and her Jeri curl dripped on her shirts. She had 8 grandchildren of all ages from 16 down to 2 years old. There were so many of them, and they all sang in the choir. Sister Baxter had two daughters and a son, and all of them were on drugs. The whole family was ghetto and rude, most weeks showing up late, disrupting service trying to find one pew empty for the whole family to sit on. The Baxter grandchildren were weird, and their clothes were dingy. They wore wrinkled suits and dresses or school uniforms that had not been cleaned. Grandma Mabel was always offering to give them our old clothes, but Sister Baxter was too proud and always declined. I think they secretly didn't like one another, and

Grandma would offer just to get under Sister Baxter's skin. They tried to be cordial, but you could see the tension between the two of them.

Grandma Mabel used to help some of the children at church. She would buy them winter coats, hats, and gloves, making sure we had coats too. She explained that some of the children's parents were on drugs and they were being raised by their grandparents or relatives. Growing up, I thought we were poor. Compared to some of the children that came to our church, we were middle class and not poor. We did not have to share clothes or shop at the Goodwill. I grew to appreciate what I had and was thankful Momma was not on drugs.

My grandparents were from the south, so being active in the church was important to them. Papa Ray was the head deacon, and close friends with Pastor Buford. Papa was in charge of unlocking the church on Sunday mornings, turning on the lights, and starting devotion after Sunday school. Papa started devotion with a hymn and prayer. I loved when Papa Ray prayed. Listening to him pray taught me how to pray and what to say during my prayers. I knew God was listening when Papa prayed.

Grandma Mabel was a deaconess, so she sat in the front row with the other deacons' wives. There was an unspoken contest every Sunday on who wore the best suits and most unique hats. Grandma Mabel's only competition was the First Lady, Precious Buford. Some of the other wives had nice outfits and hats, but the coordination of the shoes and accessories were just as important. Grandma Mabel was a tall woman. She had some of the biggest and most distinctive hats. Her colorful attire was a compliment to her godly mood on Sunday morning. Not one Sunday went by where Grandma was not slaying her Sunday best.

Papa Ray dressed simple for church. He wore simple black and gray suits, and solid-color ties. If you asked me, he wore the same suits over and over again just with different ties every week. Papa and Grandma never rode to church together; they drove separate cars, but met at home for dinner on days we did not stay at church all day. Papa Ray was a mystery to me. He did not speak to me often unless he wanted me to clean up something. He was a quiet man and kept to himself, only talking to Grandma when needed. As husband and wife, they had their good and bad moments. They were my only example of a married couple, and I learned a lot from watching them.

One Sunday morning, Momma was not in a good mood and had been mean to us and yelling all morning. She woke us up early to clean the entire house and she was still unhappy. I hated being at home most of the time but when Sundays came, I was ready to go to church. It was my escape from being at home, and was a good amount of time away from home.

Grandma Mabel called the house phone and told us to get ready, as she did every Sunday. Momma told me to tell her that we could not go to church because her house was not clean. Grandma was upset, and started calling on Jesus and praying for Momma. I do not think Grandma liked Momma and how she treated us. Grandma accepted that we would miss church. "Khloe, make sure you clean up and listen to your mother. Papa will come to pick y'all up later to go shopping for school clothes."

When I tried to tell Momma, she slammed her bedroom door in my face and locked herself inside. I just went back to cleaning. Once everything was cleaned, we got dressed and were ready to go.

Around 2:00 p.m., Papa Ray knocked on the side door to pick us up. I put my shoes on and walked through the kitchen toward the door. Momma was standing there yelling at Papa. "These are my muthafuckin' kids! You can't just come to get them without asking me first!" I did not know why she was so upset. Papa just kept asking her what was wrong and was talking very calmly. It all happened so quickly, but Momma pushed him down the three small stairs at the side door. He stumbled backward but didn't fall. The look on his face said it all. He looked up at me as I stood there watching their interaction. He looked defeated, and turned to walk out the door. She slammed the door shut and sat down at the dining room table. "Get y'all coats on and get the fuck out!" she yelled. I did not think she would allow us to go but we put our hats and coats on and rushed out the door.

Papa Ray usually parked at the end of the driveway. He looked up and smiled when he saw us coming out the front door. He was just sitting in his truck. He got out and opened the door for us. "Are y'all okay?" he asked as we got in. I nodded my head yes but had no words. Momma's behavior was shameful and uncalled for. The entire ride to his house, he talked about Momma. "I can't believe that girl pushed me like that. Something is seriously wrong with my daughter." He went on and on, and I just stared out the window as we rode along. I was sad, and tears escaped my eyes.

We arrived at the house. Grandma had cooked Sunday dinner. Honey baked ham, collard greens, mac and cheese, sweet potatoes, black-eyed peas, and cornbread. I was happy to sit down to a hot plate full of comfort food. Even though it was early in the afternoon, I felt better once I ate dinner.

I listened to Papa tell Grandma what happened at the house. It was embarrassing to see my mother act like that but worse to hear the story repeated.

After dinner, we rode an hour to Montgomery Ward. It was Grandma's favorite store. It was a huge department store that sold everything. Grandma bought all of us school supplies, clothes, shoes, coats, and boots. I was grateful for my grandparents because Momma rarely took us shopping. We stopped at Baskin Robbins for ice cream before going home.

Grandma walked us to the door with our bags and once we got inside, Momma slammed the door in her face. I guess she was still in a bad mood. She went through all our bags but said nothing. We got sent to take showers and were told to go to bed. I wanted different parents. I wanted a different life—and a better mother.

Lying in bed that night, I cried silently. I was unhappy and wanted to know why Whitney was my mother. What did I do to deserve her? I cried all night long until I cried myself to sleep. I was mentally exhausted. I wanted to understand something, but I did not understand anything. I hated crying when I was upset, it made me angrier. I wanted to run away.

Grandma Mabel was a good role model and inspiration.

She showed me that I could do whatever I put my mind to. She was driven in her career. She balanced being a wife and a mother. She was always on the go, and helping everyone she could. I did not understand why she helped people the way she did until I was in Sunday school one morning. The youth minister told us how Jesus fed the five thousand people with five loaves of bread and two fish. Grandma Mabel was teaching me to be like Jesus by helping others. She always told me how blessed I was.

Grandma Mabel was a talented beautician. She specialized in helping women grow their hair. She took classes on Mondays when the salon was closed and traveled to different cities for hair shows and conferences. She was always expanding her knowledge and abilities with hair. Cutting, coloring, and braiding, she could do anything to her clients' hair. I became her hair model once my hair grew past my ears. She styled my hair for different hair classes she attended, and I began traveling with her out of town.

Grandma told me there was a hair show and conference in Atlanta and she wanted me to go with her. I did not want to do hair when I grew up, but I wanted to go for the experience. I had never been to Georgia before. I was not sure Momma would allow me to go but she did. I think Grandma bullied her into saying yes. It was going to be my first plane ride and I was nervous. It was not as scary as I thought it would be. Getting off the plane in a different city felt strange. Everything looked different, and we had to catch a cab where we wanted to go. We checked into our hotel downtown and I felt like royalty. I was impressed with how everyone treated me, and I knew then that I wanted to live in a different city away from home—and Momma.

During the day, Grandma went to class and I got to hang out in the hotel room. I watched movies and ordered room service for lunch. The only thing I was not allowed to do was go to the pool. After the classes ended for the day, we went to dinner at a steak house not far from our hotel. Grandma had me get dressed like I was going to church for dinner. We sat and ate with other hairstylists from different cities. Some of the women had strong accents and I did not fully understand what they were saying. I got to order whatever I wanted on the menu. It was the first time I ordered steak. It came with asparagus and mashed potatoes. When the server asked me how I wanted my steak cooked, I said, "Medium well, please." Grandma just looked at me but said nothing. I had read enough articles in magazines to know how I wanted my steak cooked. When my food came, we prayed, and it was the best meal I ever had. The steak was so tender and juicy.

One of the ladies said, "Mabel, your granddaughter is well-behaved, and even knows how to order a steak." They all laughed, and I smiled and said thank you. Grandma winked at me and that was her sign of approval.

On the last day of the conference, there was a huge hair show. It was so much fun! Each state was represented and had its own theme. They came dressed in costumes with props and their hair models. The art of styling, braiding, and cutting hair was amazing to witness. I enjoyed learning about the art of hair.

Grandma Mabel did not care for people with fair skin. She honestly could not help it. It was how she was raised, and how she raised her children. I remember hearing her say, "My daughter went and found the lightest nigga she could find to have babies with." The three of us were "light bright," as she called us. Mabel had no desire for light-skinned grandchildren. She was always threatening to put us in the sun so we could gain some color. Her dark-chocolate complexion was beautiful. I wanted to be darker too, but I did not know how to change the color of my skin.

Her main goal was putting us in the sun so we could get a tan or a shade or two darker. Grandma Mabel was raised in the south, so she was constantly making a difference between white and Black people. Momma disagreed with seeing people based on the color of their skin. She taught us that the color of people's skin did not matter. Growing up in a predominantly Black neighborhood, I only saw white teachers and a few white students at school. The color of people's skin was not a factor for me. I saw people based on how they behaved and treated me.

I wanted to feel accepted by Grandma Mabel. There were times when she made me feel like I was her favorite. Other times, I felt like she tolerated me. I was curious about everything and I asked questions. She said, "Girl, you ask too many questions. I don't have time to answer your crazy questions all day long." Whenever she did answer my questions, it was never a direct answer. Her responses formed more questions in my mind, and it only added to her irritation with me. It drove her crazy until she would just tell me to shut up. There were moments when I enjoyed being around Grandma Mabel and other times I wanted to be as far away from her as possible. The older I got, the more I understood her mentality with life. She was raised in a different era, and I had to learn to accept her for who she was.

CHAPTER 17

Once I became a teen, I felt alone. My wall of pain was up, and I didn't let people get close to me. I was cautiously curious. When I was headed to middle school, I was unsure about myself in a lot of ways. I had anxieties about everything, from making new friends, to what kind of bookbag to carry. I was no longer wearing a uniform, and could finally wear whatever I wanted to school. I asked Grandma Mabel not to curl my hair anymore. I wanted to wear it straight down instead. My appearance was important to me. I was transitioning from a child to a preteen and I was confused about a lot. I did not want to ask Momma questions because I feared her responses on so many levels. I asked Grandma Lily questions, but her experiences were different when she was a teenager. I had a few friends from school, but they were just as clueless as I was.

When I was in the 6th grade, I had dreams of becoming a fashion designer. I loved to draw and create pictures. I had a sketchbook and colored pencils that Grandma Lily bought me for Christmas. I drew dresses, jeans, and sweater designs that I wanted to have made and sold in the stores. I had dreams and goals. I showed Momma and she said, "Designing clothes is a lot of work, Khloe. You do not even know how to sew. Maybe you should pick something different to do. All clothing designers don't make it." I did not allow her words to kill my ambition. I kept drawing, and just stopped showing her my ideas.

In the summertime, the rule was, I had to be in the yard when the streetlights came on. Momma said, "If I can't see you from the door, you're too far." So as long as Momma could see us from the porch, we could stay out a little longer.

Uncle Ray bought me a baby-blue, 10-speed mountain bike. I loved my bike, and I rode it every day, all day. I enjoyed a good, long bike ride. I rode my bike for miles and explored the neighborhood. It was therapeutic, and helped me to clear my mind. I enjoyed the freedom and the exercise.

One afternoon, I was out riding my bike and I could tell the sun was going down. I was kind of far from my street. I stopped at the corner store for some snacks and a juice and took my time getting home.

Riding down my street, I could see Momma sitting on the porch. She had a belt in her hand. Damn! I was late! The streetlights had just come on. Karla and Wesley were already inside the gate playing with their friends.

She looked at me and told me to put my bike in the garage. I took my time and walked slowly toward the house. I knew she was going to whoop me. I walked past her to go into the house and she started swinging and hitting me. She did not care about my friends being outside. She whooped me in the front yard as the neighborhood kids watched. I was so embarrassed! It wasn't even that dark yet, but she always accused me of sneaking around and being fast with a boy. I could not cry, I was too mad.

I went into the house, showered, and went to bed. She told me I could not eat any of her food. I was allowed water—that was it.

Momma was super mean to me all the time. It was so exhausting, and I did not know what to do.

That night, I started a diary. I grabbed one of my old notebooks from school and ripped out the pages of academic notes. I began writing down all my random thoughts. I wrote for hours, and once she told me to turn my light off, I grabbed the flashlight from under the bathroom sink and wrote under my blanket. It was such a release, and I felt much better! I hated Momma, and I let my diary know every emotion and all my thoughts. Running away was always an option, but I was not going to end up like the people I saw on the street. I had no choice but to endure the pain. I told my diary all my deepest thoughts and secrets. When I was done writing, I placed my diary under the side of my mattress and went to sleep.

I knew what it felt like to hate and love someone at the same time. It was not a good feeling. Especially when that person was your mother. I thought she was supposed to love and nurture me. I yearned for love, emotion, and affection. Momma was not capable of showing me any of those things. It was like she secretly hated me but could not tell me. Her unresolved pain affected the relationship she had with her oldest daughter.

I struggled with my personality traits and how I reacted to situations. I was half Whitney and half Charlie. I battled with what to do and who I wanted to become. Momma raised me and guided me, but she was unable to help me with my questions and curiosity of all the whys. Why did I think this way? Why was I quick to get angry? I needed help, but did not know how to ask without getting accused of being a smart-ass.

I began writing every day. I wrote after school, after dinner, and before bed. I wrote daily so my mind was not clouded with all the good and bad thoughts swirling around, confusing me. I felt liberated between the lines of my diary. It was a total escape to a world of freedom and safety for me. I could express myself; be heard without anyone's judgment or input. I also wrote down goals and made lists. I wrote down things I wanted for myself and how I wanted to decorate my room. I had ideas about what type of job I wanted, and future goals for after college. I had dreams and big plans.

***

A few weeks later, I came home from my friend's house across the street. I walked through the front door and my diary was sitting on the couch next to Momma. She had a weird look on her face, and said she wanted to talk. My stomach instantly dropped. I felt violated. As bright and sunny as the summer day was, it instantly felt like a thunderstorm of freezing hail was hitting me in the face. I had no doubt she had read it. There was not much I could say or do. We both knew what I had written. How did she find it? *I'm going to murder Karla!*

Momma asked me to sit down next to her and then she hugged me, tightly. It was the most awkward moment and unwanted physical contact I had ever experienced with my mother. The hug felt empty. I cringed hard like she was going to hit me. I could feel the hairs on my arms raise as chills went through my body. I was more comfortable when my teacher gave me a hug. I wanted to sink into the couch and hide from whatever was coming next.

She turned the TV off and looked at me and said, "Khloe, I am doing the best I can with raising y'all. Being a single mother is not an easy job. Please don't run away from home. You can come to me and talk to me about your feelings."

She went on and on, but I stopped listening. I did not care about the conversation and I was definitely not going to express my feelings to her. I allowed what she said to go in one ear and out the other. Her words meant nothing to me. Her words carried no weight of sincerity. She said stuff all the time and did not keep her word. Like the time when she was supposed to buy me a new dress for the school spring dance and I ended up wearing last year's Easter dress instead. Or two weeks ago when she needed gas in the van and asked me for my last $20 that she still had not paid back when Friday came. I was ultimately bothered and irritated. Why would she read my private thoughts? I was offended that my privacy was penetrated. I did not care about the chat we were having. I was silent for most of it, and just listened to her lie to my face. I just wanted my diary back. I wanted some real privacy. I wanted the fake, sentimental conversation to be over.

She leaned over and kissed me on my forehead and told me that she loved me. All I could think about was where I could hide my diary from now on. My feelings were hurt, and she had no clue how to help me or fix me. The tender words

I love you meant nothing to me. Daddy said it all the time and it meant absolutely nothing. Now Momma was saying it while hugging and kissing me. I was getting this attention and affection because she read my inner thoughts and secrets and she felt guilty. I did not believe any of her words—at all.

She'd never treated me like this before, and it turned out to be a one-time special because the affection never happened again.

It was awfully hard for me to listen to her words when her actions showed me differently. It was do as I say, and not as I do. I would hear what she said, but the example she set was not what I wanted for myself. I was lacking healthy guidance from my mother. I did not know what I needed from her but as I paid attention, I knew that I could not trust her. I did not want to be anything like my mother.

We moved around so much that by the time I completed the eighth grade, I had attended six different schools. Every year for middle school, I went to a new school. It was hard making friends and not be able to see them when school started. Talking on the phone and hanging out at school were two different types of friendships. I was not allowed to go to any of my friends' houses unless they lived in our neighborhood. Momma was too busy to meet my classmates' moms, so I was not allowed to attend sleepovers or birthday parties with my friends. She did not care about my feelings or if I had friends or not. Everything was all about her, all the time.

The summer of my 8th-grade year, we moved again. We moved into a bigger house, where we all had our own bedroom and two and a half bathrooms. The neighborhood was different from where we moved from. It was ghetto, and full of drug addicts and crime. I hated the new neighborhood. I liked our old neighborhood better, but my opinion did not matter to Momma, so I kept it to myself. There were a lot of children that lived close by, so the three of us made new friends.

On my first day of 8th grade, I was in a new school and the vibe was weird. I was the only kid in my first-period class with a bookbag. I was the only new face in most of my classes so of course, the teachers wanted me to introduce myself to everyone. I hated it! "Hi, I'm Khloe. I transferred from St. Monica's Catholic School." Everyone just looked back at me while I stood at my desk. A few of the kids turned around and smiled at me. I was glad it was over and sat down quickly. I was quiet, and just watched the other kids' behavior during class.

When the bell rang, Qiana came and introduced herself to me. She was nice, and showed me around the school. We talked in between classes and ate lunch together. We had so much in common. We instantly became friends. She was an only child and lived with both of her parents.

Qiana lived around the corner from me and we walked back and forth to school together. On the weekends, we went skating and had sleepovers at her house. Our childhoods were quite different. I thought I wanted to be an only child, but she complained about being lonely and not having anyone to play with when she was younger. She had to depend on making friends at school or visiting her cousins.

Qiana struggled in some of the classes and I helped her with homework to improve her grades. The kids were different at my new school. Qiana knew most of them from elementary school, so she had a lot of friends. I did not like some of the girls, so I kept my distance. They were her friends, not mine.

Whenever I got in trouble, it was for fighting. The girls were so ghetto, and all they did was gossip and talk about people. I got tired of hearing the lies they made up about me and others. Momma put me on punishment for fighting and getting suspended from school. I stopped caring about going outside or talking to my friends on the phone. I did not care at all. My life was starting to feel like one big punishment.

Before fall arrived, I needed a new coat. When I asked Momma, her response was, "Call yo daddy." Her response was full of sarcasm, and it was a test to see if I would pick up the phone and call him. I thought about just asking Grandma Lily, but I did what Momma said and I called him. I told him my coat from the year before was too little and I asked him to buy me a winter coat. He told me he got paid on Friday and would see what he could do. "I'm gon' see what I can do" usually meant no in my book. So, I did not hold my breath waiting for Friday.

Every day I walked home from school and was home alone for a few hours until Karla and Wesley's bus dropped them off. Momma came home around six thirty, so most evenings I started dinner. Friday around 6:00 p.m., there was a knock at the front door. We did not have a doorbell, but everybody that came to visit usually went to the side door. I asked, "Who is it?" and it was Daddy. I had a moment of excitement because he actually showed up! I quickly opened the door. We hugged, and he handed me a big, brown coat. I said thank you and he kissed me on my forehead and got back in his car, and left.

I stood at the front door and looked at the coat. It was ugly, and big. It was not in a bag, nor did it have tags on it. I wondered if he bought the coat or got it from someone. I was confused, and not sure where the coat came from. When I tried it on, it was two sizes too big for me. I could not fit the coat and it was ugly. I thought back to when he bought me underwear that was too small. He did not ask my size or what color I liked. I always heard Grandma say, "It's the thought that counts," but I was unhappy and did not want to be ungrateful. I hung the coat on the dining room chair and went to my room to finish my homework.

After dinner, Momma was sitting in the den with her bottle of wine, catching up on her soaps. "Khloe! Come here!" she yelled. I rushed downstairs and she asked, "Whose coat is that hanging on the chair?" She pointed.

"Daddy dropped it off earlier but it's too big for me," I said. I picked the coat up and put it on so she could see how it fit.

Momma set her glass down and stood up. She put the coat on, zipped it up and it fit her perfectly. "Where's the bag, and why did you take the tags off?" she asked.

"That's how he dropped it off," I responded, shrugging my shoulders. The look on her face was just as confused as mine was when he dropped it off earlier.

Later on, when I was washing the dishes, I heard her on the phone laughing with Robyn about the coat. "Girl, Charlie is such a dumbass. You should see this coat he dropped off to Khloe. He probably went to the Goodwill." She was laughing so hard. My feelings were hurt. I was disappointed with both of my parents.

The *Sunday Plain Dealer* was a big deal to Momma. She gave me $1.50 to walk to the corner store to buy the newspaper. She would sit and read through the newspaper, look at the sales, and clip coupons. I was upstairs cleaning my room when she called me downstairs. "Look at that paper right there," she pointed. I grabbed the Value City store sales paper from the couch. I looked at the front and flipped it over to the back. The words were in big, yellow letters, "BIG & TALL." A tall, bald-headed Black man was wearing the same coat that Daddy had dropped off to me. I felt my heart flutter. No wonder it was so big on me. It was a man's coat! Momma found it funny, but my feelings were hurt all over again. I put the coat back on the chair and went back to my room.

Later on that day, Momma took me to Value City to return the coat. The cashier looked at her like she was crazy when she explained that the coat was purchased but we did not have the tags or a receipt. The cashier handed me a store gift card. Momma and I looked through the racks of coats, and I tried on a few. I could not find a coat that I liked that fit me. I was upset. I wanted to just pick out a coat, but they were all for older women.

After a while, Momma ventured off to another section and picked up a few things for herself. I was determined to find something I wanted. I found a pair of house shoes, two shirts, a pack of gel pens, and a journal. Leaving the store, I still did not have a winter coat. I asked Momma, “So what are we going to do? Because I still need a coat.” She shrugged her shoulders and puffed her cigarette. She did not care, but spent some of my gift card on her items. Momma made me feel like not having a coat was my fault. I had done what she asked me to do. And so did Daddy, kinda.

CHAPTER 18

Uncle Ray was Momma's younger brother. He was like a big brother, and my uncle. He was 10 years older than me and I looked up to him. As I got older, I listened to his words of advice and understood what he taught me. He gave me his point of view on life and broke things down for me to understand. My questions did not bother him. He was my only and favorite uncle.

As a kid, I probably had 2–4 pairs of shoes in rotation, but that was not enough for me. As a teenager, anytime I needed new shoes, I called Uncle Ray. Momma bought whatever sneakers were on sale. I was grateful, but not happy with her choices. By the time I got to middle school, I did not want to shop at Montgomery Ward with Grandma Mabel anymore. So, Uncle Ray started taking me to go school shopping at the mall. He allowed me to pick out my own sneakers and clothes for school. He made sure the clothes fit and that I had enough to last me a few weeks.

The best shopping trips were for my birthday. He made me feel special, and always took me to dinner after shopping. Some of his friends came, but I did not mind. They were nice. I observed their behaviors and listened to their conversations. Uncle Ray did not cuss around me and did not allow his friends to say certain things in front of me either. "Aye, man, my niece right here! Don't talk like that in front of her!"

I was 10 years old the first time we went trick-or-treating. Momma told us Uncle Ray was taking us and I was so excited. He picked us up and took us to the costume store. I picked out a Wonder Woman costume. He went to the drugstore and bought us two large pumpkin buckets each. It was cold and wet outside, so I wore a black shirt and black jeans under the one-piece outfit. We drove 30 minutes away from where we lived to one of the nicer suburban neighborhoods. His lady friend went with us, and said that is where they gave out the most candy.

Uncle Ray parked his truck at the end of the block and we walked around the small, gated community until our buckets were full. It started raining and we ran back to his truck. He bought us food from Wendy's and took us home. Momma was not home, so I hid my candy buckets under my bed and filled my bookbag with some to store in my locker at school.

Once I got to middle school, Uncle Ray consistently helped Momma out by taking me shopping for clothes and shoes. Friday evening, he would call and tell me to be ready by noon the next day. I was excited, so I did my Saturday morning chores and got ready. I waited and waited. After a few hours I called, and he said that he was still coming. Uncle Ray was bad with time and didn't show up until after I ate dinner. I had an attitude from sitting and waiting for him all day. He would hug me and say, "Khloe, quit being like that." I could not stay mad at him long. I loved my uncle Ray.

Once I became a teenager, I allowed my appearance to help me with maintaining my self-confidence. I was into my appearance, so I always washed and ironed my clothes every day and kept my shoes clean. Once I got to the eighth grade, I was old enough to catch the bus to the mall. Uncle Ray started bringing me money instead of taking me shopping. He would always come past everyone's bedtime, when we were usually asleep. He called the house phone nonstop until someone answered and opened the door for him. He walked into the kitchen, opened our fridge and freezer, and shook his head. He handed Momma a stack of bills and told her to get some groceries in the morning. He pulled me to the side away from her and asked me not to tell Momma how much money he gave me. I had no problem keeping it a secret. He gave me $300. I bought one pair of sneakers, a couple pairs of jeans, and a few shirts to match my shoes. I saved some of my money for lunches and snacks.

A few Saturdays every month, Uncle Ray, called super early in the morning, would ask Momma to get up and open the door at 7:00 a.m. The vibration from the bass of his music shook the house as he backed his truck into our driveway. He popped his trunk and rolled two suitcases and multiple duffle bags into the living room. "Whit, count everything up for me and I'll be back to pick it up around two," he said. She would agree and lock the door behind him.

As I was sitting at the kitchen table eating my cereal, Momma called me to come help her. I watched as she unzipped the bags one by one and all of the bags were full of money. It was so much money! Some of it was wrapped in rubber bands, folded neatly, and the rest was balled up. Momma asked me to help her sort and separate the bills into piles. Each denomination went into stacks of 100. It took hours to sort and count the money. My hands were tired and dirty before we finished. Momma did not ask questions about the money and Uncle Ray did not volunteer any information about it. They had a system and it worked. All Momma cared about was her profits from her counting duties. I was curious but all I knew was that Uncle Ray was a sophomore in college.

CHAPTER 19

It was not often that Momma took us to her friends' houses. She introduced Ronald Jefferson to us as Mr. Ron. He was a cool, laid-back guy. I knew she liked this dude when we started spending weekends with her at his apartment. He had three older children and had been married and divorced a few times. I was not sure how old he was, but I knew he was a lot older than Momma.

She told us she was "in love" again. I could tell something was going on because she was acting differently again. She was being nice to us more than usual, cooking and cleaning like she did it as regular behavior, trying her hardest to impress her new man. Mr. Ron had a nice apartment full of figurines and milk crates full of old records. He worked first shift at a factory, and was the opposite of all the other guys that she introduced to us. They spent a lot of time together and with us as a family. He began helping Momma with buying groceries and school supplies. When she needed brakes on her car, Mr. Ron took her car to his mechanic and Momma did not have to pay for anything. Mr. Ron was nice to us and treated Momma differently, with respect.

After a year, Mr. Ron told me he was going to ask Momma to marry him. I was happy and asked him, "Does that mean I will be your daughter? Will it change my last name too?"

He chuckled at my questions and told me, "Yes, if that's what you want, baby girl." We hugged, and I told him that I was okay with them getting married.

After dinner one Sunday, Mr. Ron got down on one knee and asked Momma to marry him. She said yes! A few months later, he moved in with us and they began planning their wedding. She cooked dinner more often and they were happy together. It was good to see Momma finally genuinely happy. Momma was a lot better, and her happiness meant she was nicer to me. Our home was now peaceful and felt normal, like the families on TV. I began to appreciate my new home life.

Mr. Ron and Momma drank every day. He came home after work with two bottles of her favorite wine. He would mix up his special cocktail after dinner and they listened to music and drank. He would play music and slow dance with Momma in the living room. Some weekends, they went out to parties and bars together. They went on dates to the movies and hung out with his family and friends.

They never really argued or yelled at one another, at least not in front of us. He was a quiet man, but his voice was deep and stern when he spoke. He was nice to me, and I appreciated having him around. Mr. Ron would tell me how I reminded him of his daughter. He said he was not able to see her often when she was growing up. I was curious and wanted to know why, but I did not want to hurt his feelings by asking too many questions. I enjoyed the feeling of having a dad, even though he was not my real dad. It was weird at first, but Charlie was never there for me, so I adopted Mr.

Ron and accepted him as my stepfather. We were a family.

The summer before I was going into sixth grade, they got married and went on a week-long cruise for their honeymoon. Mr. Ron started discussing having a baby with Momma. Mr. Ron had two older sons and a daughter, but was never with their moms to be able to raise them. He was helping Momma raise us, but he wanted his opportunity to be a father to a baby of his own. Momma was against the whole baby conversation 100 percent. Kids were a nuisance to Momma, and she was already stuck with three. She told him no, and ran out and got a dog from the local animal shelter instead.

I don't know who wanted a dog, but Momma thought it would soothe Mr. Ron's request. It did not, and Mr. Ron wanted nothing to do with the dog. I did not want a dog, nor was I interested in having to clean up behind it. It was Wesley and Momma's dog, but neither wanted to clean up and take care of it. Momma didn't let him in the house too often unless it was raining or wintertime, so he was an outside dog that was always dirty and barking.

Every day after school, Mr. Ron was home from work because he went super early in the morning. One day I came home from school and was in the kitchen making something to eat before starting my homework. I could hear his footsteps, and then he called me upstairs. Mr. Ron usually watched TV in the living room and when I came home, he asked me how my day at school was. I felt comfortable talking to him. At 3:00 p.m. every day, he watched *Maury*. It was his favorite show, and sometimes I would watch it with him. We guessed at which man was not the father of the baby, laughing at the story line and eating snacks together before everyone else got home.

The bedroom door was open and he was lying in the bed. I walked into the bedroom and he asked me to lay down next to him. I told him I had a lot of homework to do and he replied, "Just lay here with me for a little while. Come watch *Maury* with me."

I hesitated at first, but did what he asked and walked slowly toward the bed. I laid down close to the edge of the bed and I felt his big arm around my stomach as he pulled me closer to him. I was uncomfortable and wanted to get up. He slowly began rubbing my arm and then his large, rough hands eased across my growing bosom. I could feel something poking me on my lower back.

At that moment, I was frozen in fear. I was afraid to do anything, and no words left my lips. I closed my eyes tightly and wished I could get up. He did not say anything, he just rubbed my breasts and my arm. We lay there for what seemed like forever. My body was stiff, and I felt paralyzed. His breathing got heavy and his breath was hot on the back of my neck. I could feel wetness forming between my legs like I had to pee. I blankly stared at the TV, wishing the moment was over soon.

I heard the garage door close and then the side door slammed. Thank God, Momma was home. He jumped up quickly and raised his voice at me. "Get out of this room, and you better not say anything to anyone." The look on his face was serious and scared me. He had never talked to me like that and I did not know what to do. I just stood there in shock. He rushed me out and I went to my room and closed the door. I felt violated, and my feelings were in a weird space mentally. I started crying, but I was not sure why I was crying. I kept thinking, what did I do wrong? I was not comfortable telling anyone. I thought about telling Momma, but I didn't know how to say it. I was not sure she would listen to me if I did try to explain to her what happened in her bed with her husband.

After that, I started coming home later than I was supposed to, just to avoid being home alone with Mr. Ron. I got yelled at and put on punishment almost weekly for coming home late but I did not care. I was uncomfortable being alone with him.

Mr. Ron taught me to appreciate all music. He grew my passion for music because he listened to all types of music, from R&B, hip-hop, jazz, and gospel. Music was a mental escape from my reality. I loved music.

CHAPTER 20

Karla and I had talked about running away a few times but agreed not to do it. A few weeks after she started sixth grade, she ran away. I could not believe it! I had thought about it a hundred times, even caught myself planning it out but Karla executed it—for days!

That Wednesday morning, we all left home headed to school. Karla and Wesley went to two different schools because Wesley had gotten kicked out of the public middle school they were attending. Wesley caught the private school transportation van, while Karla and I caught the public bus but in two different directions.

After school, we usually got home around the same time but when Momma came home around 6:00 p.m., Karla still was not home. Momma always had a bottle of wine waiting for her after work. She changed her clothes and began drinking and pacing back and forth. Mr. Ron was working two jobs, so he was not home a lot. She called Robyn to come over and to bring more wine. We all were concerned about Karla's whereabouts as it got later into the evening. I stayed in my room, listening to the conversations between Momma and Robyn. Robyn always had man problems, but Momma wasn't trying to hear it today because Karla was missing.

Robyn said, "Whitney, are you listening to me?"

Momma went off! "Bitch, my daughter has not come home from school and you sitting up here talking about a nothing-ass nigga! It is time for you to leave. I can deal with this alone."

Robyn apologized, and I heard her footsteps going down the back stairs.

"KHLOE!" Momma yelled. I walked to the kitchen to see what she wanted. "Call Karla's friends and ask them if she was in school today." I called all the numbers in Karla's purple phone book, but none of them saw her at school since the day before. All of them said she missed school today and did not know where she was. The look on Momma's face showed that she was worried.

Around eight thirty, Momma called the police. That is when everything got real for me. I was scared for my little sister, and could not believe her boldness. It took the police 20 minutes to come. They knocked on the door so hard we all jumped. Momma gulped down the rest of her wine and rushed to the bathroom. "Khloe, please open the door for them. I have to brush my teeth," she said. I could tell she was stressed, nervous—and drunk.

I sat at the table, looking at the two police officers. They looked around the living room at the photos on the walls as they waited patiently for Momma. One cop was an older, chubby white man and the other was a tall, dark-skinned young cop.

Momma came downstairs crying, and the officers began their questions right away. It was painful to listen to her struggle to answer their questions. She had no idea what Karla wore to school that day. Momma did not get up with us in the morning to see us off, and her drunk ass couldn't remember today from yesterday at this point.

The police looked at one another and before they could say anything, I butted in. "This morning, Karla had on dark-blue jeans and a yellow t-shirt. Her jacket is navy blue and red, and her shoes were blue and white."

They both were scribbling on small notepads as they watched Momma's movements. They both handed Momma a card and said to call them if she heard any information. Momma was crying as she walked them to the door.

Other young girls had gone missing in our neighborhood, and most of them never made it back home to their families. I watched the news and thought it was so sad. I never imagined that my family would ever go through the same thing. I did not want us to be on the 6 or 10 o'clock news, crying and begging the public to help us find my little sister.

That night, I could not sleep. I lay in bed, thinking about where Karla was all night. Did she eat? Where was she sleeping? I was worried. Lying in bed, I just stared at her bed and all her belongings. Her things were always on the floor all over her side of the room. Sharing a room with someone that was missing felt awkward. I got out of bed and cleaned up. I made her bed and straightened our room up. By the time I was done, I was ready to get some sleep. As much as Karla got on my nerves, I wished she were home in her bed snoring right now.

When I got up for school the next morning, I looked over at Karla's empty bed and just shook my head. She did not come home last night. I could not believe it was real. I looked in Momma's room and Mr. Ron was already gone to work. Momma was asleep on the couch with her cigarettes and half-empty cup right next to her.

I got Wesley up for school and avoided answering most of his questions. He was in bed when the police came last night so I just told him that Karla did not come home and that I didn't know anything else. I honestly did not know what to tell him. I did not want him to be worried about Karla while he was at school. He was bad enough, and did not need anything to add to his behavior problems.

The police told Momma that they could not issue an Amber Alert because Karla was considered a runaway and had not been kidnapped. They also told me that I was not allowed to mention anything to anyone at school or any of Karla's friends. Momma had to inform her school the next day, but the police said to do it in person and not over the phone, so she took the day off. Momma dropped me off and I could tell that she had cried all night. Her hair was in disarray and she looked worn-out in her wrinkled jogging suit. Her big eyes were being held open by puffy eyelids and her expression was empty and blank. I wondered what was going through her mind as I got out of the car and headed into school.

I heard a horn beep and when I turned around, Momma rolled the window down and shouted, "I love you, Khloe!" I just smiled and waved. Yeah, she was worried.

My friends asked me why I was so quiet at lunch and during my classes. I lied and told them I was not feeling well. It was not a full lie, I just kept thinking, where was Karla? It was one of the longest days of school and I was unable to focus on anything.

I usually caught the bus home, but Momma was there to pick me up; maybe she thought I was going to run away too. As I walked to the car, I prayed that Momma was going to say that Karla had come home. She did not. Momma asked me if I knew where Karla was or if I had heard anything at school. We did not attend the same school, so I did not understand why she was asking me those questions. I felt like Momma thought that I knew where Karla was, but the truth was, I didn't know anything. I was worried too! If I did know something, I would have spoken up at this point because I was scared for my little sister.

We rode downtown to Momma's job. She said she was going to print flyers with Karla's picture. The police were not willing to get involved with a runaway, so we had to find her on our own. Momma talked to Uncle Ray while we were in traffic and he told her to offer a reward because it would help people keep an eye out for her. I told Momma that Karla talked to Sister Baxter's grandson on the phone. They were supposedly girlfriend and boyfriend at church, but they didn't live close or go to the same school. We stopped by all her friends' houses, and no one had seen Karla since Tuesday; it was now Thursday.

Pulling up to the house, I could see Uncle Ray's big, blacked-out truck sitting high on 26-inch black rims parked in our driveway. He jumped out smelling like weed and a thick cloud of smoke vanished with the wind. He hugged me and kissed my forehead. Uncle Ray was about 6'3", slim, with a muscular build. He was always calm and smiling.

Momma talked quickly and he cleared his throat and crossed his arms as he was taking in everything she was saying. Once she started crying, I just walked toward the house. "Whitney, calm down," he said. I wasn't about to get emotional, so I left them hugging in the driveway and went inside the house.

Wesley was sitting at the table doing homework. Uncle Ray had picked him up from the lady's house across the street before we got there. I fixed a bowl of Apple Jacks and Wesley started with his questions. "Khloe, how come Karla ain't coming home yet? Do you think she's dead?"

I just stared at my little brother as he asked his questions so nonchalantly. "Boy, don't let Momma hear you say that stuff and no she ain't dead! We're going to find her and she's coming home soon." I spoke with a lot of confidence and uncertainty. I wasn't sure of my own words, but I couldn't let him worry or repeat those words in front of Momma.

Momma and Uncle Ray walked into the house. Her eyes were red and puffy, and he had a serious look on his face. "Khloe, do you have any idea where your sister could be at?"

I stuffed cereal and milk in my mouth and shrugged my shoulders. Did my family think I knew and was not saying anything? I dropped my head because I started crying. "No, Uncle Ray, I'm really worried about Karla too."

He hugged me and told me to stop crying. "We're going to find Karla and bring her little bad ass home!" He handed Momma some money and said, "Fill your tank up and get them something to eat. No drinking, Whit! I'll meet you across town around eight." Uncle Ray kissed Momma on the cheek and walked out the door.

Momma called in an order for one large deluxe pizza and she sat at the table smoking one cigarette after another while we finished our homework. I'm sure she wanted to have a drink but was listening to Uncle Ray's orders. I sat and watched her as she ate three slices of pizza, drinking pink lemonade, and smoking cigarettes back-to-back. She looked stressed-out! All I could think about was where were we going, and where was my sister? If no one knew where Karla was, where were we meeting Uncle Ray at later? I had so many questions going through my mind, but I knew now wasn't the time to ask.

Once it got dark, we got dressed and Momma drove in the direction of Grandma Mabel's church. As we rode in silence, I looked out the window at the cars riding past. Everyone was going somewhere and dealing with something. The city streets were lit up with lights and traffic was busy.

Wesley was asleep in the backseat by the time we parked. We parked in front of this house, and Momma turned her headlights off. She picked up her cell phone and called Uncle Ray. "Yeah, we're here. The lights are on in the living room and I can see movement inside the house." I just sat silently and paid attention to see what was going to happen next. "Okay," she said, and they ended the call.

We were on a stakeout to find Karla. I did not know what

house Momma was watching but after 15 minutes of sitting, I saw a big, black truck flying down the street past us. It was Uncle Ray. He jumped out with a gun in his hand and this big Black dude wearing all black got out of the passenger side. They went to opposite sides and walked around the house to the backyard before coming back and banging on the front door. I could not see who opened it, but the door was slammed in their faces. Uncle Ray jumped in his truck and sped off.

Momma's cell phone rang, and I jumped. Momma just held the phone listening and said, "I'm not leaving without my daughter, Ray!"

I tapped her leg when I saw the police pulling up. "Ray, this bitch called the police on you! I'm gon' fuck her up!" she shouted.

I heard Uncle Ray shouting, "Calm down, Whit, we're going to get Karla back!"

I wanted to cry but it was not going to help the situation so I held it in. I wanted to help but I did not know what to do. We sat there in the dark watching until the police left. I was finally able to see whose house we were at: the evil choir director from church, Sister Baxter. I knew she was a demon in a choir robe! She stood on her porch smoking a cigarette, watching as the police left her street. She did not see us watching her. She had a short body and was hunched over as she limped back into the house, slamming the door. Another long ten minutes we sat until the living room light went off and then we drove away.

Momma smoked and drove in the direction of home. She flicked her cigarette out the window and finally spoke. "Khloe, we think Sister Baxter is allowing Karla to stay at her house. We're coming back over here in the morning, so when we get in the house, take your shower and go straight to bed."

It was chilly, and Momma had all the windows cracked because she was smoking nonstop. I rolled my window all the way down so I could breathe some fresh air. I hated the smell and smoke of cigarettes. I wondered if Grandma Mabel knew what was going on with her favorite church member. I was just ready to see my sister again and for all this drama to be over.

The next morning, Momma woke me up early like it was a school day. We dropped Wesley off at school and drove back across town to Sister Baxter's neighborhood. Momma handed me a stack of flyers she had printed. They had Karla's picture on it and read "MISSING" in big, bold, red letters. The flyer had a description of what she was wearing, a $2,000 cash reward, and a phone number listed. It hurt my chest to see that, but I had faith we were going to find her and bring her home.

Uncle Ray and a few of his friends showed up and helped us canvas the two blocks. This older man was sitting on his porch across the street from where I was, and I saw him waving Uncle Ray down. I crossed the street so I could hear what the man was saying. "If y'all looking for that little girl, she may be in that house right there." He pointed, and simultaneously, we all looked. It was an abandoned house right behind the house we were watching last night. "The Baxter family has always owned that house and the one they live in on the other street. That woman cannot control all of those children and when she kicked her daughter out of the house a few years ago, it's just been sitting. Every day I see those badass grandchildren of hers running in and out. Go knock on her door on the other street, she might be home." Uncle Ray showed the man a picture of Karla, but he said he hadn't seen her but would keep an eye out.

Momma was crossing the street toward us as we walked off his porch. I heard Uncle Ray giving the man his cell phone number and telling him to call him anytime. "What did he say, Ray?" Momma asked.

"He told us Sister Baxter owns this abandoned house right here. He said her grandchildren be in there sometimes."

Momma turned and looked. "Baxter lives in the one behind it," she said.

"I know, we're going in!" Uncle Ray went to his car, grabbed a crowbar, and we all followed behind him as he kicked the side door down on the raggedy house. The smell was nasty, like old pee and dead cats. The house was still set up with furniture but was dirty and dusty. It was filled with rolls of carpet, and trash was all over the floor.

I pulled my hoodie up to cover my nose. I wanted to throw up from the smell, but I was ready to find my sister.

Some of the windows were missing as we walked through the living room. It was obvious that someone had been in the house. The sofa was worn but had pillows and blankets, as if someone recently slept there. As we were going up the stairs, the smell got worse. Three bedrooms were full of old furniture, rolls of carpet, and a toilet sitting in the middle of the hallway—full of piss and shit! It was disgusting! I ran back down the stairs to get some fresh air. I couldn't take it!

She was not in the house, but that did not mean she had not been there. Momma and Uncle Ray were not too far behind me as we walked back to the cars. The street was quiet, and no cars were coming or going. It was so unusual, like an eerie suspense movie feeling. Where was Karla?

We got back in the car to ride around the corner to the Baxters' main house. It was daytime, and we were no longer keeping a low profile. Momma lit another cigarette and as cold as it was, I had my window rolled down. I did not want to die from secondhand smoke before we found my sister. I felt like I could still smell the stench from that house on my clothes. Ugh!

The house was quiet as we rode past slowly. Uncle Ray told Momma not to bother Sister Baxter since she called the police on him last night. Momma flicked her cigarette into her yard. "I want to kick this old bitch ass so bad! All my life she been in church, hooping and hollering for Jesus, and over here allowing runaways and her badass crack baby grandchildren to do what the fuck they wanna do!" Oh yeah, Momma was pissed off.

Her cell phone rang; it was Uncle Ray. "Whit, meet me at the diner on Hayden." Finally, some food. I was starving.

As soon as we got to the restaurant, I went to the bathroom to wash my hands. We sat at a table near the big window and looked over the menu. The waitress brought us water and gave us a few minutes to decide what to eat. One of Uncle Ray's many phones began to buzz on the table. He picked it up, jumped up and yelled, "Come on!" He threw a $10 bill on the table and ran out the door.

We jumped in the cars so fast, Momma did not even have time to light a cigarette as she ran all the traffic lights and stop signs back toward the Baxters' street. Uncle Ray was already parked in the driveway of the old man he had talked with earlier, and Momma parked right in front of his house. The old man stood up and pointed toward the abandoned house. "They just went in there about five minutes ago!" he yelled anxiously.

I watched Uncle Ray jump out of his truck with his large, black pistol in his hand. Momma and I got out of the van and waited. Shakily lighting a cigarette, Momma began sobbing. Oh Lord, here we go, I thought, rolling my eyes.

Uncle Ray walked straight into the house like it was his. Time felt like it froze as we waited for him to come back out. What was only a few seconds seemed like forever at that moment. The anticipation was driving me nuts!

I saw them first and ran toward Uncle Ray, Karla, and Clifford Baxter. They both looked scared. I hugged Karla tight. I could hear Momma behind us crying and hollering as she walked across the street toward us. I looked at Clifford and when he smiled back at me, I kicked him right between his legs! He fell over on the ground I jumped on top of him and began punching him in his stupid-looking face. He just lay there and took every punch. His lip and nose started bleeding and I kept punching and screaming at him. I could hear Karla screaming stop.

Uncle Ray grabbed me. "That's enough, Khloe!" I kept kicking and trying to stomp his slow ass through the grass he was laying in.

Picking me up and carrying me to his truck, Uncle Ray looked at me. My heart was pounding, and I was trying to catch my breath. I was pissed off! "Khloe, you need to calm down. We got Karla back now." He hugged me and looked at me and said, "You whooped his ass good though." He smiled, and we both laughed. My adrenaline was pumping, and I was ready for round two. Uncle Ray grabbed a towel from his truck and told me to wrap my hand up. I did not realize my knuckles were bleeding.

I was not sure why Karla's ass was crying but she needed her ass kicked too! She had all of us worried to death. Momma was hugging Karla as they sat in the van, crying and rocking back and forth. I looked across the street and Clifford was finally getting up. I was ready to run and kick his ass some more, but my hand was sore and Uncle Ray said no. "Khloe, reach in the backseat and grab that bookbag please." I handed him the heavy bag and followed him onto the porch with the old man.

"Young lady, you got some fire in you," the old man said as he gave me a high five.

"Thanks for looking out for my niece and calling me," Uncle Ray said, reaching into the bag and handing the man two hefty stacks of cash. He gave him $5k in fives and tens.

The old man's face lit up and he quickly stuffed the money into his coat pocket. "Thank you, young blood," he smiled. He stood up, shook Uncle Ray's hand again, and went inside his house.

I was ready to go home. "Uncle Ray, can I ride with you?" I asked, hoping he would say yes. I didn't want to ride back with the crying crew but I had no choice.

"Not right now, Khloe. I got some business to handle. I will stop over later to check on y'all. I'm proud of you today, you're a good big sister," he said as he winked at me. I had never heard that before and it meant a lot to me. I did not even care about riding home with Momma; Uncle Ray's words gave me bliss at that moment.

Once we got home, Momma sat in the bathroom with Karla while she took a bath. I wanted to stand by the door and listen, but they were in there too long. After her bath, she lay down in her bed. I warmed up some soup and took it to her. "Are you okay?" I asked. Karla nodded her head and took the warm bowl and paper towel from me. My little sister did not want to tell me what happened, but I was curious about what she went through.

I was shocked that Momma did not whoop her or even yell at Karla once she came home. I kind of wanted her to because if I had run away, she would have beat the shit out of me! I heard her telling Robyn that she did not flip out because she was too afraid that she would run away again.

Karla did not give me any details of what happened while she was gone for those three days. She kept her distance, but I had drawn my own conclusions. I knew that she had had sex for the first time. Our house was a lot different after the drama died down. Momma and Mr. Ron started taking us out on the weekends for family bonding time. She did not make Karla clean up, no extra chores, no type of punishment.

CHAPTER 21

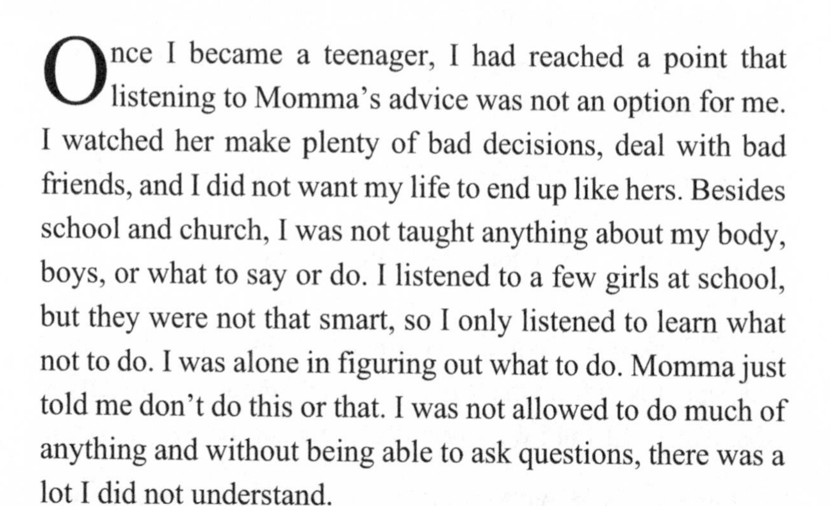

Once I became a teenager, I had reached a point that listening to Momma's advice was not an option for me. I watched her make plenty of bad decisions, deal with bad friends, and I did not want my life to end up like hers. Besides school and church, I was not taught anything about my body, boys, or what to say or do. I listened to a few girls at school, but they were not that smart, so I only listened to learn what not to do. I was alone in figuring out what to do. Momma just told me don't do this or that. I was not allowed to do much of anything and without being able to ask questions, there was a lot I did not understand.

I loved school and church, so she didn't have any problems with me. Overall, I was a good kid. I had an attitude at times, and reminded her of who she hated the most—Daddy. I fought the boys in the neighborhood because they were the big brothers I did not have. I did not like the boys at my school and definitely not the ones at church; they were all weirdos.

At 14, I was eager and ambitious enough to start working and making my own money. I found a job that paid cash under the table at the end of the day every Saturday. I was excited, because it meant I could buy my own clothes and shoes. I wanted to learn how to save my money too. Momma was glad to have me out of the house and working. One less thing for her to pay for.

On Saturdays, I worked with other teens from other schools and neighborhoods. I was gaining exposure to the real world. I was the youngest of our crew, but I managed. My height and maturity made most people think I was older than I was. For the most part, I kept to myself. I was not shy at all, and just observed the other teens while we worked.

I remember the first time I saw him; I felt my stomach drop a little. He had a big Kool-Aid smile and was as chocolate as a Hershey's candy bar. He was tall and slim. Kyle was 16 years old and went to high school on the other side of town. He talked to everybody, all day long, at work. He only talked about football and girls. He never shut up!

One day we were on the same bus together, headed to work. He saw me when he got on and sat right next to me. I was nervous as hell, and did not know what to say. Kyle was easy to talk to. We talked about movies and fashion. We had a lot in common. We both laughed at everything and nothing. We became friends. I wasn't allowed to talk to boys on the phone, but he gave me his number anyway. He told me to call him so we could coordinate riding the bus together on the weekends that we worked. Momma said I couldn't have boyfriends until I was in college, but I wanted Kyle to be my boyfriend. He was handsome, and made me laugh. I enjoyed hanging out with him.

One Saturday afternoon, Kyle asked me to go to the movies after work. It was a quick yes, and I was excited. It was the first time anyone had asked me out, but I was not nervous. Momma wasn't expecting me home for a few more hours so I had time to catch a movie.

After we got paid, we caught the bus to the mall. He paid for our movie tickets and we shared a large popcorn. I felt like I was on a date with my boyfriend, just like the other couples that were walking through the mall. The small theater was dark and empty except for Kyle and me. He put his arm around me as the movie started. We went to see *Not Another Teen Movie.* We laughed and ate popcorn.

I kept feeling him look over at me, but I kept watching the movie and shoving popcorn in my mouth. I felt him lean over and he kissed me on my cheek. When I turned to look up at him, Kyle kissed me again, but this time he shoved his huge, sloppy, wet tongue into my mouth. I did not know what to do so I pushed his face off of mine and asked him to stop. He had caught me off guard and it was too much, too fast. I thought about getting up and leaving but I did not want to make him feel bad. The moment was super awkward, and we went back to watching the movie.

He waited a few minutes, and then he started rubbing my leg. He leaned in close to my ear and whispered, "So, have you done 'it' before?" The truth was, I did not know what "it" was and no I hadn't. I only heard the girls talk about "doing it" when we were in the locker room at gym class or on the bus. I never knew what "it" meant. I lied and said yeah, and that was like a green light for him. Kyle began rubbing up my shirt and grabbed my breast. Everything was happening so fast. I could see the bulge in his pants, and he forced his lips and tongue on top of mine. I liked Kyle, but it did not feel good to me at all. I was trying to push him away. He was stronger than me. I had so many thoughts going through my head. I asked him to stop but it went unheard.

He laid his jacket on the floor and pulled me onto the floor next to him. He said, "Just relax, I know what I'm doing." He just kept kissing me and I wanted him to stop. His hands were moving so fast and I did not feel him pulling my pants and underwear down. That first moment of him forcing himself inside of me was the worst pain ever! It hurt like hell and I begged him to stop. He held my wrists down as he humped me faster and harder. I was in so much pain and I cried for him to stop.

"Kyle, please stop! You're hurting me!" I was not ready to "do it." Kyle was pushing harder as he lay on top of me and I just cried. I felt defeated and wanted it to be over. I cried louder and he eventually slowed down and stopped.

He just looked at me as he stood up, pulled his pants up, and walked out of the movie theater. I fixed my clothes and sat in my seat and cried. I jumped when the lights came on in the theater. I did not understand what had just happened. It all happened so fast, and I was left in a daze. I was in pain and felt disgusting. I walked out of the small theater with my hoodie over my head. I sat at the bus stop and cried.

I sat in the back of the bus, silently crying. It was a long, 30-minute ride home. I just stared out the window. It was late, and I knew I was in trouble. Momma was not worried, she was pissed off.

I got off the bus and could see Momma sitting on the porch. I did not want Momma to ask me anything because I didn't have anything to say. I walked toward the house and tried to fix my face. I walked into the house and she started yelling and screaming at me. I just broke down crying again. "Where the fuck have you been? It's ten o'clock and my fourteen-year-old is walking in my muthafuckin' house like she grown!"

I silently stood still as tears rolled down my cheeks. My body was sore, and I prayed to God she didn't beat me. All I could do was look at her. I just stood there as she screamed at me. No words escaped my mouth. I truly had nothing to say. I felt her cold hand and fingers slapping the right side of my face. My spirit was broken. I wanted the day to end. I wanted my life to be over. I was in so much mental and physical pain. "Get the fuck out of my face with your fast ass!" she yelled. She lit a cigarette and went back to watching her TV show.

Karla was in bed and looked concerned when she saw me. "Oh my God, Khloe, are you okay?" I could hear worry in her voice. I nodded yes and went to the bathroom. I sat on the toilet and almost screamed! There was so much blood in my underwear, and it had soaked through to my jeans. I started crying again. I stayed in the bathroom for what seemed like hours because I had to wash my clothes out so Momma would not see the blood. I took a long shower and bleached down the bathroom. I stuffed my soiled, wet clothes to the bottom of the hamper and went to bed.

That night, I just lay in bed staring at the ceiling. I felt ashamed and was mentally alone. Emotionally bruised and physically in a lot of pain. I could not sleep because every time I blinked, I could see Kyle's face while he was on top of me. I felt tortured and afraid within my thoughts. My voice was silent. My virginity was stolen from me. No one was there to console me or help me to restructure my mind. I felt unworthy and embarrassed. I could only wonder what I did wrong and why Kyle took advantage of me like that. I wanted to kill myself.

Thoughts of ending my life and not feeling any more pain overwhelmed me. I prayed and asked God to heal my mind because I knew suicide was a sin. I was forced to move on with my life as if nothing happened. I was done crying about it, and couldn't speak about it, so I buried all of the pain deep down inside.

The following weekend, Momma asked why I was still home and not getting ready for work. I wanted to ignore her question so I didn't have to lie. "I quit last week. I have too much homework to keep up with a job right now," I said. It was enough for her to leave me alone and not ask about it again. She did not mention work again, since my education was more important. The truth was, I could not face Kyle after what he did to me. I did not want to deal with anything from the job, so I avoided it altogether. I no longer wanted a boyfriend.

I had saved over $400 from working, and Momma took me to her credit union bank to open a savings account. Most of the time when she went to the bank, we stayed in the car. On this day, it was just the two of us. The bank teller asked for Momma's driver's license and my birth certificate. Once the lady entered all my information into the system, she asked me how much I wanted to deposit. I looked at Momma. I did not want her to know how much I was putting into my bank account. "One hundred dollars," I said quickly. I had brought all of my money with me, but I did not want Momma to know how much I had. Momma smiled at me and the bank teller said, "Khloe, you are going to do good with your savings account." I smiled back.

A few days later, I caught the bus to the credit union to deposit the rest of my money. The bank teller smiled at me and said, "Nice to see you again, Ms. Randolph. How can I help you today?" I placed $350 on the counter and asked her for a deposit slip. She showed me how to fill it out and gave me my account number. I was saving to buy a car, but I did not want Momma to know.

CHAPTER 22

The summer I was headed to high school was rough at home. Momma was busy with the loss of her job and trying to hold onto her marriage that was falling apart. She was not even trying to find a job. It was uncomfortable to have her home more and I could tell she was bored. Mr. Ron was unhappy, and paying all the bills by himself. Everything added stress to their marriage and created new arguments.

They began spending less time together and barely looked at one another. I noticed when they stopped going out and being affectionate. I liked our family. Mr. Ron was good to Momma and he took good care of us. On his days off, Mr. Ron stayed in their bedroom with the TV remote in one hand and his special cocktail in the other. He was drinking more than usual, but kept to himself and stayed away from Momma. I continued to keep my distance from him, but we barely saw him because he was always at work. He was not happy working two jobs. They argued because he was not getting enough rest or be able to enjoy his days off. They argued about finances, and our once perfect family unit was now crumbling.

At some point, Momma began showing Mr. Ron that she did not care about him or their union. Although he was providing and being the man that she needed, she was rude and started being disrespectful. His once small flaws were the highlights of her world and she acted as if she was perfect and he was beneath her. I paid attention to how she mistreated him. The yelling and verbal disrespect got worse. Momma was showing me how to lack respect for men, no matter how good they treated me.

One hot Friday in July, Mr. Ron came home from work. He was getting off from his first job to change his clothes before heading out to his second job. Momma was sitting in her usual spot on the couch, smoking her cigarettes and watching her afternoon soap operas. He greeted her as he always did and said, "Hey, Whitney, do you mind making me a sandwich? I just need lunch for my next shift. I'm going to shower and get ready real quick." She looked at him but did not respond. She kept watching TV and got up when she heard the water stop in the bathroom. He came downstairs and was ready to go. Momma was only halfway through making the sandwich and packing his lunch. I was paying attention to their interaction and taking mental notes. I heard her rudely tell him, "Ron, next time you need to make your sandwiches for the week. It's too damn hot to be in this kitchen." She did not want to do anything, and found a reason to be rude all because she had to get up off her lazy ass and assist her hardworking husband. She did not like being interrupted when her shows were on. "You're not prepared for work and it's not my fault. You could've asked before right now," she said with an attitude. Nothing was ever her fault.

He was a quiet man and he tried not to raise his voice with her, especially in front of us. He looked at her and yelled, "Whitney, all I asked was for a little help before I have to go back to work!" He was mad, and had her attention—and mine too. He grabbed his keys and slammed the door behind himself. He left the lunch she was working on sitting on the counter in front of her. Momma finished making the sandwich, grabbed a bag of chips, and enjoyed lunch. Poor Mr. Ron, was all I could think. What a bitch Momma was to him. Her behavior was so uncalled for and I did not like how she mistreated him.

After school one day I came home to them arguing. Momma was yelling about some woman that had been calling his cell phone. Mr. Ron looked up and saw me standing there witnessing everything. He stopped himself from whatever he was going to say next. I went to my room and pretended to do homework. He spoke calmly and said, "Whitney, I'm leaving you for good this time. I am exhausted with your bullshit. This marriage is over!" I was not shocked, but what did he mean, this time? I knew she had been giving him a hard time and he was fed up.

He walked up the stairs and went to their room. I could see their door was cracked open from across the hall. He was gathering his clothes from the closet. He cried silently. I had never witnessed a man cry before. He took his glasses off and sat on the side of the bed, shaking his head as his large hands trembled. I knew Momma was downstairs on the phone, most likely with a drink, telling Robyn what happened. I walked into their room and sat on the bed next to him but kept a good distance between us. "Mr. Ron, please don't leave us," I said as tears slowly rolled from my eyes.

He looked at me and said, "Baby girl, as a man, I cannot be disrespected by your mother any longer. I have a lot of pride, and I cannot continue to put it to the side for a woman that does not appreciate me. I have hit my breaking point, and it is time for me to move on. I must do what's best for me. I need to be happy again. I don't want to leave y'all but I have to, for my own peace of mind. I love you and your siblings, but your mom and I are done."

I started crying because I understood everything he was saying, and I felt his pain as he spoke through tears. He was hurting, and the trauma came from someone that he loved. They made vows to love and honor one another through good and bad times. "Khloe, please never allow anyone to disrespect you, you don't deserve it. You are a special young lady and very headstrong. I know you will be successful in life—once you get away from your mother."

It was overwhelming to watch him pack his belongings. Half of the closet was now empty, and he was putting his shoes in a tote. I was sad for him, but more for me. Mr. Ron had been a good stepfather to me for the past five years.

He told me he did not want to see Momma fail so he paid the rent and bills for the following two months. He was doing it to give her time to find a job. Momma was losing a good man because of her attitude and toxic ways. She changed once she lost her job and I knew that once he left, things were going to drastically change for us all over again. He left the house on a Wednesday, and Momma was back at the bar with Robyn on Friday. Old habits returning before the divorce was even filed.

CHAPTER 23

I attended a different school from my friends in the neighborhood and was barely able to see them on the weekends. My best friend, Qiana, had a boyfriend, Evan. She told me all her secrets. They had been dating for a year and were already having sex. I was not interested in having sex, but I did want a boyfriend just to hang out with. Qiana, her cousin, Imani, and I were hanging out at my house. Momma was at work, and gave me permission to have Qiana over. I had cleaned up and made lunch for Karla and Wesley.

Qiana and Imani walked over and we sat on the porch. We walked to the store for snacks and when we got back, Qiana asked if Evan and his friend could come over. I said yeah. I knew Momma was not getting off work for a few more hours and they all would be gone before then. I knew better than to have them in the house. Karla and Wesley were watching a movie and knew I was outside with my friends. Imani helped me set up chairs in the garage as it started to rain.

Evan and Tony were best friends, so they joked around together. Tony was not cute, but we were all laughing and hanging out. When it got stuffy, I lifted the garage door halfway to allow some fresh air to come in. Tony was standing up, dancing and being silly. As we laughed, the side door of the garage swung open. Robyn walked in and said,

"What the fuck is going on, Khloe?" She stood there with her hand on her hip as she looked at the five of us. Momma must have sent her to check on us and I knew I was in trouble. I told her we were just chilling. "Khloe, you need to go in the house and your friends have to leave right now," Robyn said sternly. We were not doing anything wrong, but I knew she was going to tell Momma everything and add her own twist to the facts.

I put the chairs away and gathered the trash up and went into the house. Qiana and Imani sat at the kitchen table while they waited for Imani's mom to pick them up because it was raining. Evan and Tony walked up the street toward the bus stop.

I could hear Robyn on the phone with Momma. "Yeah, she was out there with fast-ass Qiana and some dusty lil niggas!" Robyn stared at me while she talked on the phone. I just sat on the couch and waited.

When Momma got home, she was calm. It was weird. She walked past us in the living room and went upstairs. She said nothing, but I could hear her moving around upstairs. When she came back down the stairs, she had changed her clothes. She was wearing a t-shirt, jogging pants, and sneakers.

I was watching TV and felt her grab me by the back of my hair. "Get the fuck up!" she yelled. She was smacking me in the face as she pulled my hair. "You wanna be grown? You got niggas in my muthafuckin' house?!" She put her fist up like she wanted to fight and began punching me. I just took one blow after another. She punched me in my stomach and chest. She was fighting me and daring me to hit her back.

"Oh, you mad? You wanna swing on me?" SLAP! She slapped me in the face and just kept hitting me.

I was angry and wanted to hit her back, but I knew better. She grabbed the belt from the couch and whooped me. I cried and my body went numb. Robyn sat and watched like it was a movie. There was nothing I could do but take the beating. I felt like I did not do anything wrong. I did not break any of her rules. Momma beat me up like I was not her daughter.

CHAPTER 24

Marlon was my first boyfriend. I met him in the middle of my freshman year. I used Robyn's address, so I was able to attend a different high school from everybody in my neighborhood; it was Momma's idea. Her goal was to get me away from my friends. Every day after school I had to catch the bus home, crossing the street with my peers and waiting at the bus stop. They usually sent two buses because there were so many students depending on the public transportation to get home or go to work after school.

Marlon was always at the bus stop when school let out and while I waited for the bus with my friends, I kept catching him looking at me. He was tall and skinny, with a medium golden-brown complexion. He wore dark-blue skinny jeans and a fresh, white tee with Jordans and a Cleveland Indians hat. He had a big head with short, curly hair, small lips, and a nice smile. He was the pretty boy type.

When the bus came, everyone kind of formed a line to get on and he got right behind me. I could smell his cologne and the Winterfresh gum he was chewing. "I'm Marlon, but everybody calls me Marlo," he said, flashing his white teeth.

"I'm Khloe, and you are standing too close, Marlon!" I said with a smile. He laughed and moved a little closer. I smiled and tried not to laugh because we both knew he was being funny. He handed me a bus ticket so I didn't have to spend my cash and then sat down next to me as the bus pulled off.

Our conversation flowed as if we were best friends. He told me all about his parents' divorce and how he lived between their two homes. His mom had divorced his dad for cheating and getting a younger woman pregnant. His mom was bitter about the baby and made sure to receive monthly spousal support. His father drove the public bus during the week and owned a limo service that he drove on the weekends. Marlon was kept by his daddy's money, so he didn't work or hustle. His father and the new family lived close to my school and his mom lived around the corner from my house.

We talked for so long that we missed our stop. We got off and had to walk back two blocks. While walking me home, he gave me his phone number. I thanked him and when I got to my door, he kissed me on my cheek before heading back toward his house. I did not see him again for the rest of the week. He had given me his number, but I didn't call. I was nervous for some reason. I did not know what to say, so I avoided calling him and my thoughts of him.

A few weeks later he was back at the same bus stop but this time he was smiling in some other girl's face. I walked right past him and stood and waited for the bus with my friends. When we got on the bus, he came and sat next to me. The girl he was talking to at the bus stop rolled her eyes at me. "How come you haven't called me? You must have a boyfriend already," he said with a jealous tone.

"I don't have a boyfriend, but your little girlfriend keeps

looking back here. Why are you not sitting next to her?" I asked him while giving her a look back and rolling my eyes. I did not know who she was or if she went to my school.

He looked in her direction too and she waved for him to come sit next to her. He ignored her gesture and looked at me. "She ain't my girlfriend. I'm trying to give you that title," he said with a smirk. I blushed and looked out the window. She got off after a few stops and when she waved, he just gave her a head nod. This time, we did not miss our stop.

I got off the bus and started walking toward my house. "Khloe, slow down. Let me walk with you," he said.

I stopped and asked him, "Marlon, what do you want from me?"

He was taken aback by my attitude and just smiled. "I want to be friends. Do you want to stop by my mom's house for a little while before heading home?"

I was not expecting the offer. I knew Momma wouldn't be home for another few hours and I didn't have much homework, so I said yes.

His mom's house was small but decorated nicely. She had a lot of random knickknacks everywhere. She was in the kitchen cooking dinner when we walked into the house. Whatever she was cooking smelled good.

Marlon kissed his mother on the cheek and introduced us. "Ma, this is my new girlfriend, Khloe. Khloe, this is my mother, Juanita." Girlfriend? I never agreed, I thought to myself. I smiled and shook his mother's small, wet hand. Juanita looked me up and down, smiled, and asked us if we were hungry. It smelled good, so I accepted her offer. She cooked fried chicken wings, garlic mashed potatoes, and green beans. He poured us a Mason jar of red Kool-Aid and we sat at the kitchen table and ate. The food was delicious.

I looked across the table at him while he was pouring more hot sauce on his wings. "Marlon, you lied to your mother. I am not your girlfriend," I said sincerely.

He stuffed food in his mouth and said, "Not yet, but you will be soon." I just smiled and shook my head.

After we ate, I washed our plates and we went to his bedroom. It was my first time in a boy's bedroom besides Wesley. It was neat and clean, just like my room was. I sat on his big, blue beanbag and he sat on the foot of the bed waiting for his PlayStation to turn on. I watched him play the game and eventually he tossed me a controller. I looked at him, and that is when the competition began.

I knew how to play video games thanks to Grandma Lily. I got a new game system and new games for Christmas every year. We played *Street Fighter*, *Mortal Kombat*, and *Mario Race Kart*.

I didn't realize what time it was, but it had gotten dark outside. "I got to go home, it's late," I said. He grabbed my hand as he walked me home and held it the entire way to my house. He kissed me on my lips and told me that he would see me tomorrow after school. I just stood there as he walked away. He gave me butterflies in my stomach.

I was not sure if Momma was home. I was silently praying that she was not. But she was! I looked up and saw her standing in the window, watching me. I knew I was late coming home, but I had lost track of time having fun.

I walked through the door and smiled, "Hey, Momma," I said, praying she would not hit me.

"Girl, don't 'hey momma' me, and you outside kissing boys!" SLAP!

I stumbled back after taking the slap to the face. I instantly got mad because I had not done anything wrong. "Where the fuck have you been, Khloe?" I looked over at the clock on the stove, it was 6:45 p.m. I honestly did not realize it was that late. Marlon and I played video games the entire time and when I told Momma the truth, she slapped me again. She cussed me out, called me fast, and sent me to my room. I got in bed and cried. I cried because I wished I was anywhere but at home. I was glad I ate dinner with Marlon because Momma told me I could not eat anything out of her kitchen. Thoughts of Marlon flowed through my mind. I had so much fun spending time with him. I ironed my clothes for school the next morning and took a shower before going to bed.

The next morning, I caught the bus early enough to stop at McDonald's for breakfast before my first-period class. The same girl that was eyeing me at the bus stop was staring at me while I ordered my food. I smiled and walked toward her. "Take a picture, girlfriend, it'll last longer!" I said sarcastically.

She laughed and said, "Cute! But just so you know, Marlo is a hoe, so don't feel special." She grabbed her food from the counter and walked away. I heard what she said, but I did not let it faze me.

Marlon knew a lot of kids that went to my school and soon began introducing me to them as his girlfriend. I had seen most of them from being in the same class or the hallways but now they knew I was Marlon's girlfriend. I was a freshman, and most of them were juniors.

Marlon and I started spending a lot of time together after school. His dad gave him unlimited bus tickets, so I was able to save the bus fare that Momma or Uncle Ray gave me every week. We started catching the bus downtown to Tower City after school. We would sit in the food court and eat, walk around and shop, and on Fridays, catch a movie. Marlon was my first real boyfriend, and although we were not having sex, we kissed a lot and cuddled when we were alone. I wasn't big on swapping spit, but Marlon was a good kisser and had soft lips. He was very affectionate and passionate. He showed me a level of love that I had never experienced before.

As the months passed by, I was happy to have a boyfriend. He was my outlet away from home. I could talk to him about anything, and he treated me nice. Marlon loved Jordans, so when they came out, he bought me a pair too. We wore the same size. My shoe closet was quickly filling up. We had a few pairs of matching Js and he insisted we dress alike on our dates. He was my best friend, boyfriend, and favorite person to hang out with. We argued at times about dumb stuff, but he would always apologize and buy me things to make it up to me.

For my 15th birthday, Marlon borrowed his stepmom's car and took me to Red Lobster. It was my first time, and was fancy for two high school students. I appreciated how he catered to me. He bought me a K diamond gold necklace and gave me a birthday card with $200 inside. I wasn't able to fully explain my emotions, but I felt like I was falling in love.

That night was the first time that I had sex with Marlon. My only sexual experience had been with Kyle and it was traumatic. I was extremely nervous, but I knew I wanted it to happen. We both loved each other, and he told me he did all the time. Marlon was gentle with me and a perfect gentleman. We kissed a lot, but I would always stop him before things went too far. This time I didn't stop him, and I allowed him to lead the way.

We lay in his bed, kissing and rubbing on one another. I could feel the intensity rising between my legs. He stood up and took his shirt and jeans off. I was ready. My hands began to shake, and he stopped. "Khloe, are you okay? We don't have to do this if you're not ready," he said softly.

"I'm okay, just super nervous. I want to do this. I love you, Marlon."

He kissed me lightly on the lips and said, "I love you too." He began removing my shirt and bra and slid my jeans off. We both were in our underwear as we kissed and rubbed our bodies against one another. He went to his knees and asked me to relax. My hands were still shaking as he slid my panties off. His bedroom was dark, but I could feel his wet mouth on my clitoris. At first it tickled, and I let out a laugh. I relaxed and focused on how good he was making me feel. My body was experiencing something new. I was moaning as he licked and sucked between my legs. He stopped and kissed my thighs and went back to licking and sucking my clit. I could feel myself getting wetter and wetter—and then he stopped.

He grabbed a condom from his drawer and lay on top of me. I was not ready, but I could feel his penis was hard. He kissed my lips and slowly pushed himself inside of me. I tried to relax, but it hurt. He softly kissed me and said, "Try to relax, baby."

He took my hands and placed them on his back. He moved back and forth slowly as he watched my facial expressions. This was quite different from the sex with Kyle. I was enjoying the moment and could not stop moaning. He went fast and slowed down, and I scratched his back. We kissed and sexed for what seemed like forever. It was the most blissful moment that I had ever experienced, and I didn't want it to end.

When it was over, we lay together and he asked me how I felt. A few tears rolled from my eyes and I told him I was fine. I got up to use the bathroom. I was not sure if I was going to bleed again. He knocked on the door and handed me towels. We took a shower together and had sex again.

A few weeks after my birthday, I landed my first cashier job at the mall. Working after school and on the weekends taught me a new level of responsibility and independence. I was good and quick at learning everything my manager taught me. On Fridays when I got paid, I used my mall discount in the stores to get what I wanted for my wardrobe. I bought Marlon a few outfits and shoes for the both of us. I made a vow to myself to always look my best. With Marlon buying most of my shoes, I was able to save money and buy more clothes to match my growing sneaker collection.

Momma stopped buying my clothes when I started working. I still called Uncle Ray at times but for the most part, it felt good to do it on my own. I worked when I was not at school, so I was rarely at home. Telling Momma I was at work gave me a lot of freedom to explore and do things that I wanted to do. I felt like a grown-up.

Marlon became very possessive of me. He was already meeting me at the bus stop after work and walking me home from school every day. Some days he met me after school just to ride the bus with me to work. He began trying to tell me what to wear. Making comments about how I should dress more like a girl, and not a tomboy. I enjoyed my jeans and sneakers, but all of a sudden, he wanted me to wear more skirts and dresses.

All this new attention was smothering me and as much as I loved Marlon, I wanted some space. I was not sure how to tell him, but I had to say something. I wore a dress and sandals here and there just to please him but some days, it felt like it was not enough. He still was not satisfied with my attire. It was like he wanted me to become someone different, someone I was not. I continued to make efforts because we loved each other, and I wanted our relationship to work.

One humid summer afternoon, we were sitting on his mom's porch. I saw three girls walking down the street and his mom stood up and said, "Oh shit," before walking in the house. Marlon's energy shifted and he was annoyed when he saw the girls too. I had no idea who they were, but I was soon to find out as they walked toward the house. I was not a fan of drama. He stood up from the stairs when they got in the front yard. All three of them looked at me but only one got in his face. She was chubby but it was obvious she was pregnant. She was wearing a tight fitting blue dress and dirty white Chucks.

"Why you not answering my calls, Marlo? And who is this bitch sitting in my favorite chair?" she yelled while looking dead at me. He pushed the girl out of his face and they went on the sidewalk to argue. She yelled at him about some stuff she left at his house and not taking her calls. He kept saying it had been over for months. I was sitting down just watching the other two girls as they both watched me. I was irritated with the interaction and was on ready! Listening to the two of them argue about their relationship had my blood boiling. I could only wonder how many months ago their breakup was and why she was still acting like this.

Juanita's drunk ass returned to the porch and greeted the girl like she was her long-lost best friend. "Hey, Jocelyn!" she said extra loud. His mom did not care for me and the feeling was mutual. I walked past Juanita and went into the house to grab my bag. I was going home. Fuck this shit!

I stepped out the door, and I told Marlon I was going home. His mom and ex were sitting on the porch sipping wine coolers and laughing like two old friends. The drama had ceased, and I was more than glad to remove myself from the situation.

Marlon walked me home and we argued the whole way. We had been together for the past eight months but clearly, he was making time for her. "Marlon, is that your baby she's carrying?" I asked, dreading to hear the truth. He did not lie to me; he told me it was possible. I was now unsure about our relationship, and the words of that girl at McDonald's replayed in my head. My emotions and thoughts ran wild and I wanted to slap him. He kept apologizing, and I stayed silent and walked faster. He hugged me and kissed my cheek before I walked into the house.

My feelings were hurt, and I felt my heart break. I cried that night and ignored his calls for the rest of the week. I did not want to talk to him. He knew my work schedule so I asked my manager to change it so I could avoid Marlon popping up on me. It worked for a good week and then he just stalked me. He apologized and said he was not cheating on me. He was not sure if he was the father of Jocelyn's baby. I wanted no part in his drama-filled situation.

About a month later, Momma called me to come to get the house phone. I did not know who it was because everyone called my cell phone.

"Hello?"

"Hey, Khloe, it's me. Baby, I miss you so much. I wanted to share my good news with you! I had a DNA test done and the baby is not mine!" It was Marlon. I had been ignoring him and he was bold enough to call the house phone. I listened, but I was not intrigued. He asked me if he could come over to sit on my porch and talk. As bad as I wanted to say no, I said yes. There was a part of me that was missing him too. I told him to come by in an hour.

We got off the phone and I rushed to get dressed. I had just bought a cute t-shirt dress and gold flat sandals. I styled my braids, laid my edges and put on lip gloss. When he got to my house, he had flowers, a teddy bear, and a card with money inside. I could not stop smiling. I was happy to see him, and I wanted what we had back. So, after six weeks apart, we were back together.

Marlon had started working a factory job during the week from 3–11 p.m. I was happy because he was at work during the day and not breathing down my neck like he was before.

On Fridays, after my shift was over at the mall, I got my nails and feet done. On the weekends, Marlon and I went shopping. We tried new restaurants and had fun dates together. I enjoyed our quality time together and we were happy again. He was not as possessive, but he was still crazy about me.

I spent the weekend at his house. Momma was busy with her new boyfriend and stayed with him on the weekends. Karla and Wesley were preteens, so she wasn't in a rush to get home. She did not know that I was spending the night with Marlon. I just had to beat her home, which I mastered.

Momma had a conversation with Juanita once, so she was aware that I was spending time at her house with Marlon. I was not sure if Momma was okay with me having a boyfriend, but she did not give me a special talk or any grief about it.

One Sunday I woke up and the house was quiet. Marlon was still asleep, but his phone kept buzzing. I hesitated to pick it up, but I kept hearing a little voice telling me to pick it up. I opened his text messages and read the most recent ones sent. He was messaging a girl named India. I sat and read their messages. Everything Marlon and I were talking about doing together, he was saying the same things to her. Good morning and good night texts every day. The random I love you texts. Their conversation confirmed a relationship. He was texting her while we were together the day before. I was pissed! We had just gotten back together and here he was talking to another girl, again! I was ready to break up with him for good.

He rolled over and kissed me before heading into the bathroom. I rushed to save her number in my phone. When he came out, I was fully dressed. I told him Momma called and said she was on her way home, so I had to leave right away. He was salty because we had plans for the day, but I wanted to beat his ass! I went home instead of starting a fight. I did not mention India, as badly as I wanted to. I needed more evidence before I flipped out and broke up with him forever this time. Thoughts of how I was going to call her and what I was going to say rushed through my mind. I needed to know the truth. Nothing was adding up to me; we were always together. My heart was breaking.

After school the next day, I went to work and was home by 7:30 p.m. Marlon worked until 11:00 p.m., so that gave me plenty of time to call India. I was nervous but when she answered on the second ring, I got silent. I listened to her say hello and wondered if I knew this girl. Did she go to my school? Was this the girl from McDonald's? My mind raced. "Hello. Hello? Who is this?" she said. Her voice was soft. I had to say something.

"Hi, India, this is Khloe," I said. She asked me who I was and why I was calling. I said, "I'm Marlon's girlfriend. We've been together for the past year, and I want to know what is going on between y'all." I could barely breathe! My heart was pounding fast, and I felt flush as I waited to hear what she had to say.

India said, "Well, Khloe, I am Marlon's girlfriend, and we have been together for the past three months." What?! I had to keep it together and not flip out on this girl. She went on to tell me how they had been talking about moving in together once she graduated high school in a few months. He wanted them to get matching tattoos, and he was going to help her buy her first car. I was speechless! Marlon and I had discussed all the same things too. India and I were not friends at all but at that moment, we did not become enemies either. Together, Marlon was our target.

She and I talked for a half-hour and compared our stories with one another. She seemed like a sweet girl and together, we came up with a plan to confront him.

Every day he called me on his break at eight forty-five and she said he called her at nine. It was the perfect plan. I was going to ignore his call but call him right back with India on three-way. We agreed to mute our phones and listen as we confronted him to see what he would say. I was angry and nervous.

At eight forty-five I missed his call and before I could call him back, he was calling her. WOW! So, since she and I were already on the phone, she clicked me into their conversation.

He was sweet and gentle when he spoke to her. I listened to him tell her how much he missed her and could not wait to see her tomorrow when he got off work. He was truly playing both of us!

I could not hold it in any longer. I unmuted my phone and went off. "You lying piece of shit!" I screamed. His hello? response was very confused. "Marlon, how could you do this to me? You begged me to get back with you and you knew you already had a girlfriend."

India started yelling at him too. We both were emotional and upset. His bitch ass hung up and when I called him back, he ignored my call. I left him a long voicemail yelling and crying. I was so mad! I told him he was dead to me and I never wanted to hear from him again. I was hurt. I hung up the phone and cried. Marlon was the first boy that broke my heart.

CHAPTER 25

Qiana had been my best friend since the eighth grade. We did everything together. Going to the mall, getting our nails done, and shopping. She was like a sister that was my age and understood me. We shared our secrets and talked about boys. When I told her that Marlon and I had broken up, she was sad with me but said, "You're better off without him and all of his girl drama. Khloe, he was not the one for you." I knew she was right, but the heartache was painful for a while.

During our tenth-grade year, Qiana was dating this older guy, Darius. She was six months older than I was, so she was already 16. We talked about Darius and she really liked him. He was nice to her but when she said he was 25, I told her that he was too old for her. She did not listen to me and asked if I was hating on her. I was not, and it made me realize that I couldn't say anything to her about him.

She eventually stopped catching the bus to school with me because Darius began driving her to school. I declined his offer to give me a ride several times. I didn't agree with their relationship, so I caught the bus alone and walked to the building with the other kids from school.

Some days, Qiana did not show up for school. I asked our

teachers for her assignments so she didn't miss anything. When I went to her house later, she told me she had spent the day with Darius, hanging out. She was smoking weed and drinking with him. I didn't agree with her new actions and behavior, but I kept my thoughts to myself. She was changing and becoming distant because of him.

The Wednesday after we came back from spring break, Qiana called me over to her house after school. She was having a meltdown in the bathroom when I got there. I was glad her parents were still at work. She opened the door for me and grabbed my hand, rushing me to the bathroom. My mouth dropped when I saw all the pregnancy test sticks on the bathroom counter. "Khloe, I think I'm pregnant!" she said as she began to cry. I hugged her, but I was speechless. So many thoughts rushed through my head and I wanted to help her figure this out.

"Qiana, calm down. Let's clean this mess up before your mom gets home. We're going to figure this out together."

"Oh my God! What am I going to do?!" Qiana was freaking out. I was too, but I was trying to keep it together for the both of us. I put all the positive pregnancy tests in a trash bag and threw them away outside so her parents wouldn't see them. She lay in her bed and cried. "I cannot have a baby. I love Darius, but my dad will try to kill him!" She was hysterical.

I cooked us some ramen noodles and popped some popcorn. We sat in her room and talked about it. I told her the first thing to do was to tell Darius. When she called him, he was annoyed with the conversation. When she hung up, I asked her what he said. She looked at me with her puffy, swollen, red eyes and said, "He told me that he will pay for an abortion, but I can't have no baby. I am too young, and his wife—"

"Wife? Qiana, he's married? What the fuck!?" I said. My reaction caused her to cry even more. I held her while she cried. This whole situation was a disaster!

The following Friday, Darius picked her up from school early to go to the free clinic to confirm her pregnancy. She told me that Darius took her to the abortion clinic and paid for the procedure. She was nervous about getting an abortion, and I believed there was a part of her that wanted to keep the baby. I didn't fully understand or agree with her aborting the baby, but I knew she could not become a mom at 16 in the tenth grade.

We did not talk for a week after the abortion and she hid everything from her parents. I called a few times and she sent me to voicemail. She told her mom she was sick, and that was enough for her to miss three days from school.

CHAPTER 26

During high school, I remained on the Merit Roll with As and Bs. My favorite subject was English. It used to be math up until I got to high school. High school math was difficult, for no reason. Algebra II was trigonometry with letters, numbers, and equations. It was my least favorite type of math. I understood the work and was able to pass the class. I was interested in learning things that were going to help me in the future. I did not understand how solving for x to the second power was going to help me or when I was going to use it in the real world.

I continued to work at the mall three days a week after school and on the weekends. I had plenty of clothes and shoes, so I slowed down with my shopping habit. I was focused on saving my money. I was making weekly visits to the credit union to deposit my paychecks. My goal was to buy my first car before my senior year.

My high school was full of kids from different neighborhoods and ethnic backgrounds. I was making new friends and learning more about myself as I matured. When the bell rang the students gathered in the hallways, talking and laughing before our next class. Some of the boys started fights and some of the girls argued with their friends. There was always some drama in the first-floor hallway and I tried to avoid it. The lunch periods were by grades, so all of the sophomores ate lunch together. The rules did not stop the juniors and seniors from coming into the lunch line to buy snacks and food. The security guards were super cool, so they really didn't bother the students unless they were causing trouble.

As I was sitting in my 5th-period class, Spanish II, the fire alarm went off. Ms. Gonzalez told us not to panic and to exit the classroom quickly. We all got up and rushed out of the building: 2,600 students standing on the front lawn of the school thinking it was a fire drill. I knew something was wrong when I overheard one of the security guards say, "No one knows who pulled the alarm. We need to check the cameras." I prayed the building was not on fire.

The fire trucks pulled up and a fireman spoke with Principal Townsend. The fire marshal and security guards walked through and cleared the building. By the time everyone was cleared to go back into the building, the bell rang, and it was time for us to switch classes.

My last class of the day was PE. I was glad gym class was at the end of the day because I did not like changing my clothes. Before we could start exercising, the fire alarm went off again. Now I was annoyed, especially since I was wearing basketball shorts and a t-shirt. It was 50 degrees outside, and we were not allowed to grab our coats from the locker room.

The entire school was on the front lawn again and a huge fight broke out. We did not have gangs, but there were neighborhood rivals. These fools were really pulling the fire alarm so the whole school could witness a stupid fight. I didn't care about a fight; I was cold, and ready to put my clothes back on.

Some idiot continued to pull the fire alarm for the following three weeks. The fire department was obligated to come each time and they were getting annoyed with the prank. The fire marshal told Principal Townsend that he put some sort of invisible ink on all the fire alarm handles that did not wash off with soap and water. The last time the alarm was pulled, we had to wait in line to enter the building as we went through a UV light with our hands out. The stupid prank ended with a group of six freshmen boys getting charged and arrested.

We were a month away from the end of the school year and I was ready for the summer. I was sitting in my Earth Science class and noticed Bianca and Kristina were passing notes back and forth and laughing. Bianca was a mixed girl from the west side that thought it was okay to say nigga because her daddy was Black. I had a problem with it, and asked her not to say it the first time I heard it come out of her mouth. She did not like the fact that I said something to her about it. She had a big mouth, but did not want anyone to say anything to her. We were not friends.

Kristina was her sidekick, copycat, and best friend. They both kept looking back at me and I just rolled my eyes. The teacher snatched the note and said, "Ms. Coleman and Ms. Smith, since the two of you are disrupting my class, let's see what is so funny." Everyone was looking as Mr. Lesnewski read the note and then he looked up over his glasses at me. What did the note say? Now I was irritated. I had to get my hands on the note.

The bell rang and the class left. Mr. Lesnewski had the

note sitting on his desk. I walked to his desk and asked him a question about the homework assignment. "Ms. Randolph, I take it you and Bianca are not friends?" I shook my head no as I looked down at the note. "Well, I am going to refer you both to attend conflict resolution after school." I smacked my lips and snatched the note from his desk before he could stop me. It read: *Khloe is corny and didn't deserve Marlo's fine ass.* Before he could say anything or stop me, I was in the hallway looking for Bianca Coleman. Her locker was across from mine, so I headed in that direction. She was standing at her locker talking to Jayson, the captain of the football team.

I walked up behind her and said, "Bitch, you don't got to pass notes, say what the fuck you got to say to my face!"

She turned around and laughed, "Girl, bye! You must have read the note. Yeah, I wrote it. And?" Before she could get another word out, I punched her right in her mouth.

Jayson was standing there and yelled, "FIGHT!"

I was mad and kept swinging and punching her in the face. Bianca grabbed my hair and we tussled until we fell on the floor. I rolled on top of her and began choking her with one hand and punching her with my other fist. I heard Qiana screaming my name and then I was getting picked up into the air. I was kicking and yelling, "Get the fuck off of me!"

Mr. Tyson put me down and grabbed my shoulders. "Girl, calm down! Let's go," he said as he held my arm, walking down the stairs. I was trying to catch my breath. My adrenaline was flowing and my heart was beating fast. I was enraged. I felt tears rolling down my cheeks. I did not say anything as Mr. Tyson led me to Mr. Townsend's office.

I sat and listened to Mr. Townsend tell me how disappointed he was in my behavior and starting a fight. Mr. Lesnewski called Momma to tell her that I was in a fight. I got suspended for five days for initiating the fight and causing chaos in the hallway. I did not care. Mr. Townsend asked Mr. Tyson to escort me to my locker and out of the building. We walked past the nurse's office and I looked in and saw Bianca. Her shirt was ripped and her bra was showing. She had a black eye, and her nose was bleeding.

"Move it!" Mr. Tyson said as he gently pushed me past the door when I paused to investigate. We walked toward my locker and he asked, "Are you going to tell me what happened for you to put such a beating on that little girl like that?"

I looked at him and said, "Mr. Tyson, I get so sick of these catty, petty-ass girls. They talk so much shit and spread rumors about people. I was just fed up today." As the head security guard, he understood the high school drama.

I opened my locker and looked in my small mirror hanging up. I had a few scratches on my face and neck, and my hair was messed up. I brushed my hair into a ponytail and grabbed my notebooks. I packed my bookbag and slammed the door shut. Mr. Tyson walked me to the front door and said, "Khloe, you cannot solve your problems with your fists. You must learn to be the bigger and better person in situations. People are always going to have something to say about you. Fuck them! Now you have to miss five days of school for someone else's opinions of you when they don't matter in the first place."

I nodded my head and said, "Thanks, Mr. Tyson. I'll see you next week."

I got on the bus and called off from my work shift. I just wanted to go home and lay down. Mr. Tyson's words kept repeating in my head and I knew he was right. Internally, I was dealing with emotions that I did not want to deal with. My breakup with Marlon was only a few weeks old and I was still in my feelings about it. Bianca earned that ass-whooping! I was not feeling the gossip, drama, or the petty note. Everything replayed in my mind and I did not have any regrets about the fight. I was not sure what Momma was going to say about me getting suspended from school, but I did not care.

When I got home, Momma was sitting on the couch with Wesley, helping him with his homework. She looked at me and asked what happened. "I got into a fight. They suspended me for five days," I said.

Wesley started laughing and said, "So who won, because you got scratches all over your neck!" I ignored him.

Momma continued, "Well, I want to know why you were fighting. Please don't tell me you were fighting over some boy." I shook my head no and told her what happened with the note in Science class. The note was about me and Marlon, but the fight was my frustrations toward Bianca, the note, and my repressed anger from not dealing with my emotions.

I returned to school the following Thursday and had to check in at the office. Mr. Townsend informed me that he changed all of Bianca's classes that we shared and moved my locker away from hers. When I saw her in the hallway, her eye was still bruised and her top lip was swollen. Kristina gave me a look, but I ignored her. I was trying to be a better person, as Mr. Tyson said.

The last week of school was so fun. The Student Council organized the Oscars and a talent show. The Oscars were awards for Best Dressed, Cutest Couple, and Most Likely to Succeed. They passed around a survey during homeroom so everyone had a chance to vote. I didn't care about the Oscars; I was excited about the talent show.

The sophomores and juniors sat in the middle section of the auditorium. The freshmen sat on one side and the seniors sat on the other side. Not many seniors came, as they already had prom and were done with their classes for the year. Principal Townsend got on stage and gave us the rules. "No screaming, no booing, and no fighting. Let's have a good time and enjoy our classmates before the summer starts." Most of the students were talking to their friends and not listening to Mr. Townsend.

The talent show went by class, so the freshmen were first. Only a few were brave enough to get on stage in front of the whole school. Two boys decided to rap, and a set of twins sang a gospel song, and everyone stood and gave them a standing ovation.

A few of my classmates got on stage, but Rico Hernandez stole the show. Rico was the only Puerto Rican on the football team. He had long hair, and his body was nice and muscular. He came out in a black leather vest, leather pants, and a black cowboy hat with matching boots. He turned on Ginuwine's "Pony" and was dancing like a stripper. All the girls were screaming and going crazy! He tossed his hat into the crowd and was whipping his hair around while he was twerking and dancing. I was impressed, and laughed at everyone's reaction. The female teachers were chatting among themselves, but Mr. Townsend sat with a poker face.

When Rico took his vest off and snatched his pants off, the music stopped. "That's enough, Mr. Hernandez! Thank you for sharing your talents with us today," he said firmly as he handed Rico his pants.

The bell rang and we cleared out our lockers for the year. I was officially a junior.

CHAPTER 27

One of Momma's lawyer friends owned a small chain of dine-in restaurants on the west side of town and they were hiring. That summer, I was hired to work as a hostess and server. I was no longer making minimum wage and I was earning cash tips. I was able to save more money. I was motivated to get my license and buy my first car. I caught the bus back and forth to work. The bus ride to work was an hour long one way. I did not mind riding the bus, but I was ready to start driving everywhere.

Momma offered to take me and pick me up on the weekends but it was so she could get gas money from me. I only asked her when it was raining. The restaurant was in a neighborhood full of whites and Hispanics. I was gaining exposure to a whole new culture and group of people that I had never interacted with before. I loved my new job, and would pick up shifts all the time just to stay away from home and to make more money. I worked six days a week during the summer and three days a week once school started back up. I was able to keep up with schoolwork and work in the evenings.

The restaurant hosted hiring events every few months due to staff quitting for different reasons. The managers would sit in the lobby and offer jobs on the spot. Staffing was a consistent issue, so I saw many people come and go.

One Saturday morning, I came in to a new guy working in the kitchen. He was tall, chubby, medium-dark caramel skin, and smiled with deep dimples. He was cute. Throughout the shifts, we worked and made eye contact with one another. On Sundays, I worked mid-shift, so I caught the end of the breakfast and the start of the lunch rush. While I was waiting for a customer's order, Lance smiled and asked me if I could get him a fountain drink. I could see the smoke from the hot grill and he had sweat dripping down his face. He wiped his face with a towel he kept in his back pocket. I grabbed a large to go cup, filled it with ice and sweet tea and handed it to him. He smiled at me and said "thanks." We talked throughout the day, and he gave me his phone number before I left work.

Lance offered a few times to take me home after work, but I declined. He asked why I had not called him. I did not have a reason why not, so I just laughed it off and told him I would.

A few weeks later, I was tired and took Lance up on his offer of a ride after a late Saturday shift. We talked and laughed all day at work but riding in the car was quiet. There was an awkward silence between us. Everyone at work would tell me how he had a crush on me. We were not usually on the same shift but whenever we worked together, he began to drive me home.

Within that first month of talking, we started dating. We had a few movie dates when we were off from work together. Lance was sweet. He paid to get my hair braided and gave me money to get my nails done. When I started school, I only saw him on the weekends at work. We talked on the phone when I got out of school every day. Lance was a few years older than I was, so he was done with high school and had just finished trade school.

Lance lived in a two-family house. He rented out the downstairs and lived upstairs. I would tell Momma I was staying at Qiana's house and would spend the weekend with him. Our relationship moved fast. Once we started having sex, it changed a lot between us. He wanted me to practically move in with him. I knew I couldn't, and I didn't want to either.

After about two months, he quit working at the restaurant. He still picked me up from work to take me home or to hang out. I kept his house clean and cooked food for him and his friends. His friends and their girlfriends would come over to smoke weed and drink on the weekends. We all had fun together.

I stopped going to church when I became Lance's girlfriend. I didn't think it was right to go to church on Sunday after partying with my boyfriend all weekend.

He took me to meet his family one Sunday for dinner. His mom was sweet, and a great cook. His father worked two jobs, so he was getting off one, changing his clothes, and grabbing dinner before his next shift started. He did not talk much, only to his wife. Lance's sister took one look at me and said, "Lance, she's too young for you." His younger brother lived with him, so we were already cool with one another. He told me I was perfect for his big brother.

Lance confided in me about everything. He talked about his parents, his childhood, and how huge his family was. Our childhoods were very different, but we had a lot of emotions in common. It taught me to appreciate my own struggles and childhood.

One Saturday in April, I had been calling and texting Lance all day, but he was not responding. Early Monday morning when I was getting ready for school, he called to say he was in jail all weekend. He had gotten arrested for drug possession late Friday night. I skipped school and caught the bus across town. Lance met me at the bus stop. He hugged me tight and thanked me for coming over. As we walked toward his parents' house, he talked, and I just listened. He had never been in trouble before and was facing jail time. He admitted to being scared of going to jail. "Khloe, I don't want to go to jail. I've been to the county but not down the road. I can't be away from my momma, and I know she's not going to come to visit me." He was sad, and I was worried for him.

Lance's truck was towed and in the impound. I rode with him to drop his father off at work. I spent the whole day with Lance until I had to go to work. He dropped me off and came back to pick me up after my shift. I was used to us spending a lot of time together. Something changed between us though, and it came out of nowhere. Lance started picking small fights with me about nothing, all the time. We had a couple of physical fights and that was the last straw for me. He would get mad and say terrible things to me, like I did not have feelings. I was not accepting his disrespect and I was so mad that I slapped him. He slapped me back and something inside of me snapped! I started throwing punches and kicking him like I had lost my mind. He was a lot bigger than I was, but I did not care. I was pissed off! His brother grabbed me and tried to calm me down. I had a moment of sadness and cried after the fight. I cried because my feelings and ego were hurt, and I couldn't do anything about it.

Eventually, he came to his room and apologized for hitting me. I was done with the relationship. I packed all my stuff from his room. We broke up that night and I was sad about it. I cared about Lance, but I didn't love him.

I went on with my life and put my feelings for Lance behind me. I got back into my routine of school, work, and church. It was the end of the school year and I was getting ready for my senior year. I was so excited! I had saved enough money and was finally ready to buy my first car. I was looking at colleges to attend and deciding how far away from my hometown I was going to go. I had been working extra shifts at the restaurant and saving all my money.

My body began feeling different and my period was a week late. On my first day of summer break, I went to the abortion clinic. Qiana told me to go there to take a pregnancy test. I walked through the back entrance as she told me to. I paid $2 and peed in the cup. The few minutes it took felt like an hour. I was so nervous.

Two lines. Damn! It was positive.

I sat in the bathroom and cried. So many thoughts rushed through my head. I was not ready to have a baby. I was not ready to tell Momma or Lance. I was not ready financially. I had so much to figure out. How was I going to go to college with a baby? I had so many thoughts and emotions racing through my mind as I walked out the front door. There were abortion activists everywhere. I forgot I was supposed to use the back door. They were holding up posters and passing out flyers to the girls entering and exiting the clinic. Sitting in the abortion clinic, I did not even pay attention to the other girls there. I was so focused on my own situation that I did not realize most of the girls were there to abort their babies. It did not cross my mind, not once, to abort my baby. Looking at the pictures on the poster, I knew that I was going to keep my baby. I just had to come up with a plan.

CHAPTER 28

I walked to the rapid station and called my god-sister, Cassie. She was leaving a WIC appointment and came to pick me up. She had just had her baby boy a few weeks before and she was the only person I trusted with my news. As soon as I told her, she asked me what I was going to do. "I want to keep it," I said with confidence. I started crying again. I was scared. I cried the whole ride to her house.

"If you want to, you can move in with me and the kids," she said. I appreciated her having my back. I witnessed her have a baby right out of high school, and she still graduated on time and worked every day. Cassie was a good mom to her children. She was a great example to me, and I accepted her offer.

The next day, I drove her car to my house and grabbed all my clothes and belongings. Momma was not home and I was relieved for the moment. I was not ready to tell her my big news. I didn't know how I was going to tell her and I was more worried about her response. I planned to figure out a way to tell her and to avoid her until I was ready.

Once I got back to Cassie's, I called Momma and told her that I was staying with Cassie for the summer. She was okay with that and surprisingly, did not ask any questions.

I was working every day so I could save money for my

little baby. My goal for a car was now on the back burner. I had to prepare to buy baby clothes and formula.

I hesitated about calling Lance, but I knew I had to tell him. I was not sure how he was going to take the news, but I called anyway. I waited for him to answer and he did not sound happy to hear from me. "Hey, Lance, I was just calling to tell you I'm pregnant and I am keeping it." The phone was silent, and I had to look to see if he had hung up.

The first words out of his mouth were, "Is it mine?" I expected it, but was offended by it. I rolled my eyes and told him yes. He said, "I don't want a baby!" and hung up. I was taken aback by his rudeness, but I was okay with his response. The decision was mine anyway. I was just notifying him. He spoke his truth and I had to accept it. This was going to be MY baby. I was confident that I could do this on my own. I was going to be a mommy.

A few weeks later, Momma popped up at Cassie's house. We had just got home from church. I was ready to lay down and take a nap. Momma started asking me how come she had not heard from me. Why I hadn't called or come by. I did not have any answers to her questions. I knew she was going to be pissed so I told her, "Momma, I have been working a lot lately. I will come over next week." I kept hearing her voice in my head saying, *"Khloe, don't get pregnant."* It played over and over in my head while I thought of ways to tell her.

She looked me dead in my eyes and asked, "Are you pregnant?" I looked at Cassie because she was the only person I'd told. She was standing behind Momma and shook her head no.

I looked back at Momma, dropped my head, and quietly said, "Yes."

"So that's why you moved out?" she asked. She sounded upset, and I didn't want her to hit me.

"Yes. I moved out so you wouldn't put me out." Momma kept a poker face, but her eyes said it all. She was disappointed in me. I saw tears swell up in her eyes and instead of crying in front of me, she walked toward the door. I was crying, and Cassie handed me a tissue.

Momma wiped her face and said, "Well, you can come home when you're ready." She walked out the door and sat in her car and cried in the driveway. I felt a little relieved that Momma knew, but I was in no rush to move back home. I was not sure how she was going to treat me knowing I was pregnant and still in high school.

Cassie told me I could stay if I wanted to. I was happy to have her support. "Now stop all that crying before you make me cry!"

A few weeks later, I was rushed to the emergency room from work by an ambulance. I thought I was having a miscarriage. I went to the bathroom and there was so much blood. It was more blood than my period, and I knew something was wrong. I cried the entire ride to the hospital. The paramedic gave me oxygen because I told him I felt like I could not breathe. I called Momma and texted Lance. We had not been talking, but I was having his baby. I was scared, and did not want to go through it alone.

Surprisingly, they both showed up. I was scared I was

losing my baby and the tears would not stop flowing. I was freaking out! Momma wrapped her arms around me and said, "You're too young to have a baby, and maybe this is part of God's plan." I could've punched her head off! I was mentally and physically in pain and confused about the entire situation. I pushed her away from me because that was the worst thing that she could have said to me.

Lance just sat in the chair; he said nothing, and I was okay with his silence. I could feel him watching me with empathy in his eyes. Was he hoping I would lose the baby too? I regretted calling her and texting him. I wanted to be alone.

The doctor walked in and told me that my baby was fine. He explained that I was having slight complications with my uterus. There was a 60 percent chance I would make it past my first trimester, but he told me to take it easy.

I slowed down with working as much but I had diapers and wipes to buy so my routine did not change a lot. I ended up back at the emergency room two more times for the same thing before the end of my first trimester. I cried in fear of losing my baby as I sat waiting for the doctor. Every time, my little baby was just bouncing around in my stomach on the ultrasound monitor. This was my miracle baby. As much as my body was fighting off this pregnancy, my baby was fighting back harder to survive.

Momma was not thrilled about my pregnancy. She had very few positive things to say in the beginning. Once I was out of my first trimester is when I believe she fully accepted the fact I was going to have a baby. I was still at Cassie's, and not ready to go home yet. I was enjoying the freedom and happiness that I experienced living away from Momma.

My belly soon was bulging out and I was already in my second trimester without any other complications.

Momma started acting differently toward me after I moved back in. She was now nice to me, loving, supportive, and she talked to me more. She slowed down with her drinking and started staying home more. She had a boyfriend, but she was not spending as much time with him as she was before. It took my getting pregnant for her to want to teach me all the things that she thought I should know. No lessons were too late, I guess. My pregnancy grew the relationship between us, and my heart was warming up and enjoying the moments we shared. It was like meeting the mother I dreamed about; well, sort of.

We started going everywhere together. Church, grocery shopping, baby shopping, and all my doctor appointments and new mommy classes. Momma was supportive, and changed completely because she was excited to be a grandma.

I was working three days a week without tiring myself out. I tried to work as much as I could and saved every dollar for my baby girl. I was going to be someone's mother soon, and it was important to me that I'd be able to supply her with the necessities. I was a single mother and I had to prepare and plan as much as possible.

I did not experience any morning sickness while I was pregnant. I just craved good food and ate a lot. Every night after dinner, I lay in bed and rubbed my belly while reading a book to my growing baby. She moved around a lot and at times, it was painful. I thought about childbirth and the labor pains. I even watched a few videos on YouTube, but I was not mentally prepared to give birth.

As my belly got bigger, I was forced to tell the rest of my family. Grandma Lily was excited and supportive when I told her. She told me to make sure that I found a good-paying job so I could always feed and provide for my daughter. She would rub my belly and talk to my energetic baby that moved nonstop.

When I went to church, I hid my belly for as long as I could from the congregation and most importantly, Grandma Mabel. She was very judgmental, and a baby born out of wedlock was a sin. I was not ready to be judged by her scolding eye or vicious words. I was adjusting to being accepted by Momma, and the thought of feeling unaccepted by Grandma Mabel was unnerving and made me feel very insecure.

It seemed like my belly was growing every day. My senior year started, and I had only a few credits to finish up before my due date. By the time I was six months pregnant, I was no longer able to slide into the desk in some of my classes. My teachers were nice enough to allow me to sit at their desks. A few of my classmates would joke that I was having twins because my belly was getting so big. I was ready to be done with school, but I went to school every day. I was determined to graduate and figure out what was next.

Qiana and a few of my other friends helped me with baby names while we sat at the lunch table. There were girls in my class that had babies already and gave me bags of clothes. The boys in my classes made sure I ate all day and bought me snacks from the vending machines. Everyone asked to rub my growing belly, and my baby girl would just kick and bounce around all day.

Winter break was approaching, and I asked my teachers for as many assignments as they could give me. I did not want to fall behind while I was out.

My counselor set me up on the Moms First program to make sure I had the education and resources for my baby. I attended some of the classes to learn how to breastfeed and change diapers. The other girls in the class asked questions and I learned so much. The program even gave me a stroller and bathtub. I felt more and more confident that I was ready to be a mom.

Lance was not a part of my pregnancy at all. He did not attend any of my doctor's appointments, ultrasound visits, or parenting classes. He showed up a few times in the beginning when I went to the ER but that was it. I was okay with doing it all by myself, but Momma kept encouraging me to involve him. I would text to invite him, but he wanted nothing to do with me or my pregnancy.

When I entered my third trimester, there was no more hiding. My stomach had gotten so huge! I had spoken to Lady Precious, the First Lady of our church, and she sat with me and Momma so I could tell Grandma Mabel. I was nervous and afraid of her response, even though I was sitting in the house of God. Lady Precious held my hand tightly as I spoke. There was no easy way to say it, so I just blurted it out. "Grandma, I'm having a baby." My ears and neck felt like they were on fire. I needed some water and a fan.

My words caused her to stare a hole through my face and her scolding eyes forced me to look away. Her mouth dropped open and she looked over at Momma, back at me, and then at Lady Precious. "Well, I don't know why I'm the last to find out, but God bless this baby." Grandma Mabel just looked at me and shook her head.

I think she was more upset that Lady Precious knew and was present while I told her. She held her poker face but after church, she let me have it. "I don't know why you done went and got yourself pregnant, Khloe! A baby is the last thing you need, and you are not even done with high school yet. I guess you ain't going to college now, huh?! And why did you feel the need to tell Lady Precious your business? She ain't a part of this family! She gon' tell the whole damn church before next Sunday comes."

I just sat and listened to her as tears rolled down my face. Her words cut like a razor blade and my feelings were hurt. I had disappointed her, and she made it known that I did not have her support whatsoever.

The hardest person to tell was Uncle Ray. He came over to the house and after I told him I was pregnant, he just gave me a blank stare. I cried, because I knew he was disappointed. He never had anything negative to say about it. He expressed his concerns. "So what's your plan about school? Is the dad going to help you? How are you going to get around?"

He had so many questions that I did not have answers to. I was still figuring everything out for myself. I planned to finish school, and I knew how to drive but I did not have my driver's license. Lance was not in the picture at all and Uncle

Ray wanted his phone number and address. "Uncle Ray, please don't. I decided to keep my baby. He told me from the beginning that he did not want a baby, so this is on me," I said. I was taking responsibility and owning my mistakes.

Uncle Ray was frustrated but hugged me and said, "Khloe, I love you. I got your back." I started crying again.

The following week, Uncle Ray called me. "Khloe, how much money do you have saved?" he asked.

I did not want to lie, but I did not want Momma to hear the amount either. "I have to call and check the balance. Why?" I was curious.

"I found a nice car for you and the baby to get around in. I put down five hundred, and you need to bring them fifteen hundred and your driver's license," he told me. I had my temps, but I had not taken my driver's exam yet. Uncle Ray took me driving so I could learn how to parallel park. It was hard learning how to drive his truck, with the seat belt and belly in the way. I passed my driver's test and paid cash for my car. I got excited. My first car! Everything was coming together for me and my baby girl.

During my last month of pregnancy, Cassie helped me to plan my baby shower and allowed me to have it at her house. I received so many gifts for my baby girl from friends and classmates, and a few of my coworkers. Lance's mom, Stella, bought enough clothes, diapers, shoes, and supplies for her first year. Stella forced Lance to come and I could tell he did not want to be there. I ignored him and his attitude. I did not want anything from him; it was his mother encouraging him to be a part of the baby's life.

I was not sure why, but Qiana didn't show up to my baby shower. She and I had been growing more distant since I told her I was pregnant. We chose a different route for our babies. She did not tell me how she felt but I knew she was jealous. I was ready to end the friendship for good. I did not have time for bad friends, I had a baby to focus on.

I was done with work and school until after my baby came. I was at home all the time and bored. It was winter, and I was not a fan of being out in the cold. Momma said I was "nesting" because all I did was organize and clean up. Momma kept a lot of stuff—more like junk—and it was spread throughout the house. I began tossing random papers and things away as much as Momma would allow. I kept my small room clean, but with my stuff and all the baby stuff, it was congested.

During my last week of pregnancy, I was having mild contractions every day. Momma said it was not time to go to the hospital until the contractions got unbearable. I had a high pain tolerance, so I just did the breathing exercises like I was taught in the Moms First classes, rubbing my protruding belly, walking, and breathing.

Sunday morning, Momma decided to go to the wholesale club. I was tired, but wanted to go so I could walk. Every bump she hit on the way there made me feel like the baby was going to fall out.

Walking through the store, I stopped and breathed through each contraction. People throughout the store looked at me and some stopped to ask me if I was okay. Momma did some shopping and when we got back to the car, she could not find her keys. I panicked! "Where are they?" I yelled, as I was in the middle of a contraction. She searched her purse and when I looked into the van, they were still in the ignition.

I was in pain, and walked back into the store to sit down. All I could think about was the movie on Lifetime where the girl gave birth to her baby in Walmart because she got locked in the store overnight. I was freaking out in my head and trying to breathe. *Lord, please don't let me have this baby in this store!*

Momma called Cassie and she went to our house for the spare key. What took an hour seemed like an eternity with every sharp, throbbing pain. It felt like we were waiting for days as my contractions started coming back-to-back.

Once Momma started driving, my contractions were getting harder to bear. I was annoyed with every traffic light, stop sign, and bump on the road as she followed the speed limit home. I could've screamed when she slowed down at the yellow lights. If I was ever annoyed with Momma's driving, today she was doing a horrible job!

When we got a few blocks away from the house, I saw a black cat run across the front of the van. I instantly began crying. I was not superstitious, but that black cat running across our path meant bad luck. Momma tried to soothe me and just told me to pray my thoughts away. I could not hold my tears back as I rubbed and prayed over my sweet baby girl.

Momma called Karla and Wesley to come outside and help take the groceries into the house. My hospital bag had been packed and ready for two weeks, so I went to my room and grabbed it. Wesley and Karla walked me outside and hugged me. Karla smiled and said, "Good luck, sis. I can't wait to meet my niece when you get back." I was going to see them in a few days with my new baby.

I texted Lance and Stella, so they knew I was in labor. Lance did not respond, but Stella called and said she would meet us at the hospital. I wasn't sure if he would show up, but my baby was coming, and Momma said no matter what, including him was the right thing to do, so I did.

Arriving at the hospital made it all real. I had written out my birthing plan, attended all the classes, and felt prepared—until I got into the Labor & Delivery room. I was mentally freaking out. I was having a baby!

Lance and his mom arrived, and I requested that only Momma and Lance stay in the delivery room with me. Stella was mad, but it was my decision.

I informed my doctor and the nurses that I did not want to get an epidural. I wanted to try to have my baby naturally because the needle was too long, and they had to stick me in my back. I was more afraid of the needle than having the baby.

I labored throughout the night. I was not able to get up and walk around due to the baby's heart monitor. I tried to sleep, but with the pain—and Lance sitting in the corner, snoring loudly—I was awake all night. Momma was up and tried to take naps.

Lance didn't want to be there, but I was sure his mother made him. He did not have a single care about what was going on until I started screaming.

The nurse checked me and said I was fully dilated so she broke my water. My body was ready to push, and the pressure was intolerable. It was not long before my body started pushing naturally. It was time, and I was exhausted. Nurse Molly told me I had to wait for the doctor and said, "Don't push."

I yelled, "My baby is coming! What do you mean don't push?" The pain was excruciating, and I was ready for everything to be over.

"Khloe, listen to me. The midwife is in with another patient and I need you to calm down." She was calm, but I was not. Calm was the farthest thing from my mind while my body was in control trying to get my baby out. Both Momma and Lance were standing by my side, telling me to just breathe, but I wanted to push so bad. I wanted my baby to be okay, and holding her in did not feel like a good idea.

Minutes later, my midwife came in and I said, "I have to push! Please let me push!" She rushed to get her gloves and gown on while Momma and Lance held my legs up.

After hours of labor and only a few minutes of pushing, I birthed my beautiful, healthy baby girl. I named her Kennedy Randolph. I cried tears of joy when they placed her in my arms. I stared into her eyes. I held her little hand and counted her fingers and toes. My baby was perfect in every way! At that very moment, I knew what a mother's love was all about. I was now a mom and my heart was full of joy and unconditional love.

Becoming a mom at 17 allowed me to go back and evaluate everything I was taught and every example that was set before me. I had so many years of toxic behaviors to unlearn as a young woman and a mother.

Dear Momma,

Thank you! As I grow and learn more about myself, it is helping me to appreciate you more as my mother. You had your own life to live and chose to include me. For that alone, I am forever grateful. They say babies choose their mothers, and I chose you. Only God knows why, but I am happy you are mine. All the hardships and heartaches made me the strong woman I am today. I now know and understand that you were not able to give me what you did not know was missing or what I needed. I appreciate your sacrifices and the lessons. You taught me so much, and have inspired me in ways you cannot imagine. You taught me endurance, how to persevere through tough times, and determination. You showed me the strength of a single mother. Your story encouraged me to find myself and to figure out how to create the life I want and the happiness I deserve. You have motivated me to get myself together for the next generation and create a different version. I had to learn that it is okay to unlearn and do the opposite of the examples you set for me. Right, wrong, good, bad, or indifferent, you did the best you could.

I love you, Momma.

Sincerely,

Khloe

My Tributes

Rose Marie Barnes – (December 12, 1946–March 11, 2017)

Losing my granny was the hardest death I have ever experienced in my life. It took me two years to grieve before I turned my pain and anger into progress. I chose to focus on what she would have wanted for me instead of the loss of her beautiful life. I know that she is still with me; every time I see 12:12 on a digital clock, I smile and tell her I am thinking about her too.

The legacy of Rose Marie will continue to live on through me and my children.

I love you forever, Granny.

Throughout my life, I have been blessed beyond what others could imagine. I was blessed to have met all four of my great-grandmothers. Both of my parents were fortunate to still have both of their grandmothers. I was 22 years old when I lost my first great-grandmother. Grandma Lucy passed away at 98 years old. The longevity and strength of the matriarchs before me has been an inspiration to me during my adult life. I pray they are all proud of my progress as a future matriarch of this family. The legacy lives on!

Tributes: Releasing the generations of cycles from my family

Beatrice Whatley—Cousin Honey

(April 5, 1923–July 9, 2007)

Lucy L. Carter Moore—Grandma Lucy

(April 9, 1913–October 5, 2011)

Hattie Burney—Mama Tee

(November 17, 1926–March 10, 2013)

Elizabeth Webb—Big Ma

(March 7, 1922–July 20, 2013)

Marie Robinson—Grandma Big

(March 3, 1924–November 30, 2015)

Book Club Discussion Questions

1. Share your favorite quote or moment from Khloe's childhood. Why did this quote/moment stand out to you?
2. What did you learn from reading this story?
3. Would you read another book by this author? Why or why not?
4. What feelings did this story evoke for you?
5. What do you think the author's purpose was in writing this book? What idea was she trying to get across?
6. What aspects of the author's story could you most relate to?
7. What gaps (if any) do you wish the author had filled in? Were there points where you thought she over-shared or did not share enough?
8. Which scene stuck with you the most? Why?
9. What surprised you the most about the book?
10. Did reading this book impact your mood? If yes, how?

If you are interested in sharing your Discussion Q & A with the author, please send them to: 1queencarm@gmail.com

Made in the USA
Las Vegas, NV
11 February 2022